WITHDRAWN FROM STOCK
The University of Liverpool

LIST OF
BRITISH VASCULAR PLANTS

LIST OF
BRITISH VASCULAR
PLANTS

PREPARED BY

J. E. DANDY

FOR THE

BRITISH MUSEUM (NATURAL HISTORY)

AND THE

BOTANICAL SOCIETY OF THE BRITISH ISLES

Incorporating
The London Catalogue of British Plants

LONDON
1958

Issued July 1958

Price ten shillings (Interleaved copies fifteen shillings)

MADE AND PRINTED IN GREAT BRITAIN
BY JARROLD AND SONS LTD. NORWICH

G99300

CONTENTS

FOREWORD

For several reasons the publication of this *List of British Vascular Plants* is a remarkable and outstanding achievement. It is specially gratifying that, owing to exceptionally favourable circumstances, it has been possible to merge in this new work the goodwill and copyright previously attached to the three independently published yet largely similar lists of British plants. The copyright of the *British Plant List* belongs to the Botanical Society of the British Isles, that of the *London Catalogue of British Plants* is now vested in the Keeper of Botany at the British Museum (Natural History), and the Trustees of the British Museum own the right to the *List of British Seed-plants and Ferns*. The decision to incorporate these works in one volume was accepted by the Botanical Society, the Trustees of the British Museum and the executors of the late Frederick J. Hanbury who formerly owned the copyright of the *London Catalogue* and made considerable financial provision towards the cost of a new edition. This contribution has been applied to the new plant list.

Although Mr. Dandy has had the valued and willing assistance of many collaborators, particularly in specialists' genera, he has made by far the greatest contribution to this work. British botanists have been unusually fortunate in having Mr. Dandy's unequalled knowledge of nomenclature and sure taxonomic insight placed so generously at their disposal.

There has been a pressing need for a new British plant list and now that deficiency has been most worthily met.

G. TAYLOR

INTRODUCTION

By long tradition British botanists have had at their disposal numbered lists of the vascular plants of the British Isles which by their compact arrangement have provided a concise conspectus of the flora, and by their system of numbering have facilitated herbarium arrangement and quick reference to the species. The longest-established of these lists is the *London Catalogue of British Plants*, which first appeared in 1844 and ran to eleven editions of which the last was published in 1925 by F. J. Hanbury. In 1907 a *List of British Seed-plants and Ferns*, prepared by James Britten and A. B. Rendle, was published by order of the Trustees of the British Museum; this, the first list since the adoption of International Rules of nomenclature at the Vienna Congress of 1905, did much to bring the nomenclature of British plants up to date. Then in 1908 G. C. Druce, Secretary of the Botanical Exchange Club of the British Isles (now the Botanical Society of the British Isles), produced a *List of British Plants* arranged on similar lines to the *London Catalogue* but including all the casuals ("Aliens more or less fugitive") as well as the native and naturalized species; in Druce's own words, his list included "plants ranging from the most absolute native to the mere ballast waif". Twenty years later Druce published a second and much more elaborate edition of his list under the title *British Plant List* (1928), and this has since been accepted as the standard enumeration for reference in publications of the Botanical Society, which from time to time has printed additions to, and partial revisions of, Druce's list.

Just thirty years have elapsed since the publication of the *British Plant List*, and more than thirty since the appearance of the last edition of the *London Catalogue*, and in that time much has happened to the British flora, in fact as well as in its treatment by taxonomists. Some species, apparently indigenous but long over-looked, have been added to the flora; many others, of alien origin, have become established in one locality or another. Taxonomic ideas have changed, especially in the field of infra-specific classi-fication. Nomenclature, too, has undergone some drastic changes, partly because of decisions made at successive International Botanical Congresses since Cambridge (1930) and partly because British botanists have at last begun to take an interest in the precision and correctness of the names they use. Thus, for some time, the need for a new and up-to-date list has been evident. In 1946 the British Ecological Society, conscious of this need, produced a *Check List of British Vascular Plants* (published in the *Journal of Ecology* 33: 308–347) compiled by A. R. Clapham with the collaboration of many specialists, the object of which was to secure uniformity of nomenclature in contributions to the *Biological Flora* sponsored by the Society. Unfortunately this list was not numbered, and its usefulness as a standard list suffered also from the fact that its publication could not await the lengthy research necessary to achieve the desired degree of accuracy.

Since the appearance of the *Check List* there has been published in 1952 the *Flora of the British Isles* by A. R. Clapham, T. G. Tutin and E. F. Warburg, a work which has rapidly become the standard Flora of these islands and whose quality ensures that, with its future editions, it will retain that position for some time to come. With the publication of this modern Flora the time is opportune to provide once more a numbered list for the convenience of British botanists, and so the present list is put forward. It has been prepared by me in close collaboration with H. K. Airy Shaw and E. F. Warburg (fellow members of the special subcommittee appointed by the Botanical Society for the purpose) and with the valuable assistance of other British botanists who are mentioned in the Acknowledgements.

SCOPE AND ARRANGEMENT OF THE LIST

The production of a British plant list, sufficiently up to date in its scope and taxonomic treatment, has never been an easy matter; in these days of intensive floristic and taxonomic research, by professionals and amateurs alike, and along ever-extending lines of investigation, it is still more difficult. Even when it has been decided to limit the list to the established flora the questions arise how many of the very numerous introduced plants are sufficiently naturalized to be eligible for inclusion, how many species—native or naturalized—have been overlooked, and how many of the natural hybrids have been recognized and recorded. Moreover, there is the question of the system of arrangement to be adopted, there being no really satisfactory system of major classification and a sad lack of unanimity about the limits of families and genera. Most important of all, in providing a list for British botanists, is the ever-present problem of the species-concept, now further complicated by the superimposition of an uncrystallized sub-species-concept. Finally, there are nomenclatural difficulties

INTRODUCTION

which have to be resolved in order to bring the list into line with the provisions of the *International Code*. It will be obvious, therefore, that in determining the final form of the present list it has been necessary to make many arbitrary decisions, some of which may not meet with universal approval; critics may be assured, however, that every effort has been made to provide an accurate, up-to-date and satisfactory list.

SCOPE

This list, as its title indicates, is concerned only with vascular plants, so that the *Characeae*, which appeared in both the *London Catalogue* and the *British Plant List*, are excluded. The plants included are those which are accepted as being (or having been during the time of botanical recording) established members of the flora of the British Isles, including Ireland and the Channel Islands; they comprise indigenous species, alien species, natural hybrids which have arisen in these islands between species of either category, and some introduced hybrids of cultivated origin. Casuals (non-persistent adventive aliens and escapes from cultivation) are not included. It is not now always possible to distinguish between truly indigenous species and species of ancient introduction which have all the appearance of natives. On the other hand, there are many known aliens which have become established in botanical times, some very recently; the process of naturalization is always going on, and it is often difficult to decide at what stage a casual, because of its frequency or local persistence, is entitled to recognition as part of the established flora (for the period up to 1928 this difficulty is arbitrarily met by the inclusion in the list of all plants marked as established aliens in either the *British Plant List* or the eleventh edition of the *London Catalogue*). Furthermore, a colony of an established alien, and even of an apparently indigenous plant like *Diapensia lapponica*, may long remain unobserved or may not be brought to the attention of recording botanists. Users of this list are invited to inform the British Museum (Natural History) or the Botanical Society of any plants which merit addition to it.

The number of species in this list is necessarily much smaller than in the *British Plant List* (1928), which included casuals and also *Characeae*. Druce's list gave a total of over 4,250 species and "Sub-species", of which 1,706 were casuals ("Adventives") and 34 *Characeae*. The total in the present list is 2,895, which is to be ,compared with the 2,525 or so listed by Druce as natives, colonists

INTRODUCTION

denizens and established aliens (excluding *Characeae*). Both these totals are, however, swollen by large numbers of "microspecies", especially in the genera *Rubus* and *Hieracium*.[1] An analysis of the present list gives the following figures:

	Native	*Alien*	*Total*
Orthodox species	1,511	626	2,137
Additional microspecies	668	17	685
Total species	2,179	643	2,822
Additional subspecies	62	11	73
	2,241	654	2,895

In addition, 538 hybrids are recognized in the present list, including 15 introduced plants and 50 hybrids between microspecies. Druce estimated the number of hybrids in the *British Plant List* as over 500, but many of these have been found to be fanciful. The names which he attached to his hybrids are often *nomina nuda*, in which case they are not cited in the present list.

ARRANGEMENT

Major Classification

In the *London Catalogue* and *British Plant List* the flowering-plants were arranged by Bentham and Hooker's system—the one most familiar to British botanists; the pteridophytes (with the *Characeae*) were in each case placed at the end. The order of the species in the present list, for obvious reasons of convenience, closely follows that of Clapham, Tutin and Warburg's *Flora of the British Isles*, the system of major classification being the same as in that work, in which the pteridophytes precede the phanerogams and the latter are arranged according to a system based on Bentham and Hooker's but with considerable modifications designed to bring the classification more into line with modern views. In this list, however, a different concept is taken of the limits of certain families, e.g. *Lobeliaceae* are united with *Campanulaceae* and *Trilliaceae* with *Liliaceae*, whereas *Illecebraceae* are separated from *Caryophyllaceae* and *Cypripediaceae* from *Orchidaceae*; the tribe *Allieae* is transferred from *Liliaceae* to *Amaryllidaceae*.

[1] The *British Plant List* recognized 27 microspecies of *Capsella* (*Bursa*) and 94 of *Taraxacum*. These genera are not divided into microspecies in the present list, which in this respect follows the *London Catalogue*.

INTRODUCTION

The generic limits, too, are not always the same as those adopted in the *Flora*. There is ever-present controversy whether certain large "traditional" genera should be divided into smaller ones, and it is felt that in some cases, pending monographic treatment on a world basis, it is better to retain the wide concept. For this reason some of the segregates from such genera as *Scirpus* and *Bromus* are not recognized. At the same time a number of changes in generic limits are introduced following modern published treatments, or as the result of special recent study: thus *Pulsatilla* is separated from *Anemone*, *Tuberaria* from *Helianthemum*, *Groenlandia* from *Potamogeton*, and *Dactylorchis* from *Orchis*; whereas *Nasturtium* is included in *Rorippa*, *Tillaea* in *Crassula*, *Centunculus* in *Anagallis*, and *Tanacetum* in *Chrysanthemum*.

Subgenera and sections of genera are not indicated in the list as it is impracticable to do this uniformly throughout; but under *Rubus fruticosus* and in *Hieracium* "sectional" headings are inserted as guides to the grouping of the microspecies.

The genera are numbered serially throughout the list.

Species

The difficulties arising from a varying species-concept are well known, and they are nowhere more formidable than in a flora like that of the British Isles, which has been studied so minutely and by botanists of such widely differing views. There is lasting uncertainty about the claims of some plants to taxonomic recognition as species (or even as subspecies); and in particular there is controversy about the taxonomic status to be accorded to the numerous segregates (microspecies) in *Rubus*, *Hieracium*, *Euphrasia*, *Sorbus*, *Alchemilla* and other genera. Clearly it is impossible to provide a list of species to satisfy all taxonomic tastes; so in an attempt at maximum usefulness the following arrangement is adopted:

The "orthodox" species (including "aggregate" species) are listed under each genus with serial numbers in ordinary type.

The "segregate" species (microspecies, etc.) are listed under the appropriate aggregate species with serial numbers in italic type; they are also distinguished by being indented and printed in slightly smaller type.

Subspecies

Subspecies are the only infra-specific category recognized in the list. No attempt is made to list varieties and lower taxa as too few species have been studied at this level in the light of modern ideas; and in any event the working out of the correct nomenclature of these minor taxa would have caused indefinite delay. Varieties were listed in the *London Catalogue* and the *British Plant List,* but the status of most of them requires re-assessment. On the other hand, although a great deal of work remains to be done, many British species have been studied recently from the point of view of subspecific classification; and as, moreover, the subspecies of one botanist may be the species of another (as in *Asparagus officinalis* and *Ranunculus aquatilis*) they are of sufficient importance generally to be included in the list.

Subspecies recognized in the list are indented under the species to which they belong, and if a species is represented in the British flora by more than one subspecies these are distinguished by serial italic letters (*a, b,* etc.).

Hybrids

In this list a hybrid between species of the same genus is indicated by its parental formula under the species whose epithet appears first in the formula (e.g. *Epilobium adenocaulon* × *hirsutum* under *E. adenocaulon*), and where a name is also available this follows the formula and is linked to it by the "equals" sign (e.g. *Potamogeton crispus* × *perfoliatus* = *P.* × *cooperi* (Fryer) Fryer). Ternary hybrids (as in *Salix*) follow the same plan.

A hybrid between species of different genera is indicated in the same manner under the appropriate hybrid generic formula following the genus whose name is first in the formula (e.g. *Festuca* × *Lolium,* following *Festuca*), and to this is appended the hybrid generic name if one is available (in this case = × *Festulolium* Aschers. & Graebn.).

In some cases, as when a parent species is represented by more than one subspecies, the hybrid formula may cover a group or swarm of nothomorphs resulting from hybridization between the species indicated in the formula. Pending further research such hybrid groups are not subdivided in this list.

Nomenclature

Every effort has been made to provide the correct names according to the *International Code of Botanical Nomenclature* (1956). This has inevitably led to the adoption of a number of names which will be unfamiliar to British botanists, such as *Ranunculus paludosus, Thelycrania sanguinea, Centaurium erythraea* and *Echium lycopsis.* Changes like these will be received with as little

pleasure as has been experienced by those who have found it necessary to make them. It would be pointless, however, to put this forward as an up-to-date working list if the nomenclature as well as the taxonomy were not brought into line with present requirements.

Synonyms

Synonyms given in the list, whether under genera, species, subspecies or hybrids, are printed in italic type and indented under the accepted name or formula. The synonymies are not necessarily complete, being the minimum required to enable the list to be correlated with the following standard British lists and Floras and a few other modern publications:

Clapham, A. R., Tutin, T. G., & Warburg, E. F. *Flora of the British Isles*. Cambridge. 1952.

Clapham, A. R. *Check List of British Vascular Plants*. London. 1946. (Reprinted from *The Journal of Ecology* 33: 308–347. 1946.)

Druce, G. C. *The Comital Flora of the British Isles*. Arbroath. 1932.

Druce, G. C. *British Plant List*. 2nd ed. Arbroath. 1928.

Hanbury, F. J. *The London Catalogue of British Plants*. 11th ed. London. 1925.

Bentham, G. *Handbook of the British Flora*. Revised by J. D. Hooker. 7th ed., revised by A. B. Rendle. London. 1924. Reprinted 1930, 1937, 1943, 1945, 1947, 1954.

Babington, C. C. *Manual of British Botany*. 10th ed., edited by A. J. Wilmott. London. 1922.

Britten, J., and Rendle, A. B. *List of British Seed-plants and Ferns*. London. 1907.

Hooker, J. D. *The Student's Flora of the British Islands*. 3rd ed. London. 1884. Reprinted 1897, 1930, 1937.

Where a name has been misapplied in one or more of the above-mentioned works it is cited as a synonym followed by "auct.", unless it was originally published (as a new combination or substitute name) with special reference to the British plant concerned, in which case its author is cited along with the words "*pro parte*" to indicate that he misapplied it. Thus "*D. longifolia* auct." under *Drosera intermedia* signifies a misapplication of Linnaeus's name *D. longifolia*; but under *Tofieldia pusilla* the citation "*T. palustris* Huds. *pro parte*" means that although the name is inapplicable

INTRODUCTION

(its type being a non-British plant) it was originally published by Hudson in special connexion with the British species. Under *Hieracium* some misapplied names are cited as "sensu Pugsl." or "sensu Pugsl. *pro parte*", referring to Pugsley's *Prodromus* upon which the arrangement of the genus is based.

The citation of a name as a synonym means simply that the plant to which it refers is included in the taxon under which it is cited; the plant is not necessarily regarded as taxonomically identical with the type of the taxon. Thus *Chelidonium laciniatum* is cited as a synonym of *C. majus* though it is currently considered to represent a distinct variety of that species.

Special Signs

* indicates an alien taxon, i.e. one known or believed to have been introduced into the British Isles by the agency of man.

† indicates a taxon believed to be extinct in the British Isles.

‡ indicates a taxon whose occurrence as a member of the flora of the British Isles requires confirmation.

[ ] enclose taxa occurring in the Channel Islands but not known as established members of the flora of the British Isles proper.

ACKNOWLEDGEMENTS

Valuable help has been given by many botanists in the preparation of this list, and the Subcommittee's gratitude to all of them is here recorded. The following have assisted from their special knowledge of the groups indicated: A. H. G. Alston (*Pteridophyta*), G. M. Ash (*Epilobium*), R. A. Graham (*Mentha*), J. Heslop-Harrison (*Dactylorchis*), C. E. Hubbard (*Gramineae*), J. E. Lousley (*Rumex*), R. D. Meikle (*Viola, Callitriche, Apium, Salix*), A. Melderis (*Gramineae*), R. Melville (*Ulmus*), E. Nelmes (*Carex*), N. K. B. Robson (*Hypericum*), J. R. Sealy (*Caltha*), P. D. Sell (*Hieracium*), W. B. Turrill (*Centaurea*), A. E. Wade (*Myosotis*), S. M. Walters (*Montia fontana, Alchemilla*), C. West (*Hieracium*) and D. P. Young (*Oxalis*). Special thanks are due to the Cambridge University Press for permission to extract the list of *Rubus fruticosus* segregates from the manuscripts of the late W. C. R. Watson, and to P. D. Sell for carrying out the work. J. P. M. Brenan, J. G. Dony, D. H. Kent, J. E. Lousley, N. Y. Sandwith, T. G. Tutin, E. C. Wallace and D. A. Webb have made many helpful comments on the general make-up of the list.

J. E. DANDY

LIST OF
BRITISH VASCULAR PLANTS

PTERIDOPHYTA
LYCOPSIDA
LYCOPODIACEAE

1 LYCOPODIUM L.

    1 L. selago L.
    2 L. inundatum L.
    3 L. annotinum L.
    4 L. clavatum L.
    5 L. alpinum L.
        L. complanatum auct.

SELAGINELLACEAE

2 SELAGINELLA Beauv.

    1 S. selaginoides (L.) Link
    2 *S. kraussiana (Kunze) A. Braun
        S. denticulata auct.

ISOETACEAE

3 ISOETES L.

    1 I. lacustris L.
    2 I. echinospora Durieu
    3 I. histrix Bory

SPHENOPSIDA

EQUISETACEAE

4 EQUISETUM L.

    1 E. hyemale L.
        E. hyemale × variegatum = E. × trachyodon A. Braun
    2 E. moorei Newm.
        E. occidentale (Hy) Coste
    3 E. ramosissimum Desf.

4   E. variegatum Schleich. ex Weber & Mohr
    E. wilsoni Newm.
5   E. fluviatile L.
    E. limosum L.
6   E. palustre L.
7   E. sylvaticum L.
8   E. pratense Ehrh.
9   E. arvense L.
    E. arvense × fluviatile = E. × litorale Kühlew. ex Rupr.
10 E. telmateia Ehrh.
    E. maximum auct.

PTEROPSIDA
OSMUNDACEAE
5 OSMUNDA L.
  1   O. regalis L.

HYMENOPHYLLACEAE
6 TRICHOMANES L.
  1   T. speciosum Willd.
    T. andrewsii Newm.; *T. radicans* auct.

7 HYMENOPHYLLUM Sm.
  1   H. tunbrigense (L.) Sm.
  2   H. wilsonii Hook.
    H. peltatum auct.; *H. unilaterale* auct.

DENNSTAEDTIACEAE
8 PTERIDIUM Scop.
  Eupteris Newm.
  1   P. aquilinum (L.) Kuhn
    Pteris aquilina L.; *Eupteris aquilina* (L.) Newm.

ADIANTACEAE
9 CRYPTOGRAMMA R. Br.
  1   C. crispa (L.) R. Br. ex Hook.
    Allosorus crispus (L.) Röhl.

10 [ANOGRAMMA Link]
  1   [A. leptophylla (L.) Link
    Gymnogramma leptophylla (L.) Desv.]

2

11 ADIANTUM L.
    1 A. capillus-veneris L.

BLECHNACEAE

12 *ONOCLEA L.
    1 *O. sensibilis L.

13 BLECHNUM L.
    Lomaria Willd.
    1 B. spicant (L.) Roth
        Lomaria spicant (L.) Desv.

ASPLENIACEAE

14 PHYLLITIS Hill
    1 P. scolopendrium (L.) Newm.
        Scolopendrium vulgare Sm.

15 ASPLENIUM L.
    1 A. adiantum-nigrum L.
      a   subsp. adiantum-nigrum
      b   subsp. onopteris (L.) Luerss.
    2 A. obovatum Viv.
        A. lanceolatum Huds. *pro parte*
        A. obovatum × trichomanes = A. × refractum T. Moore
    3†*A. fontanum (L.) Bernh.
    4 A. marinum L.
    5 A. trichomanes L.
    6 A. viride Huds.
    7 A. ruta-muraria L.
        A. ruta-muraria × trichomanes = A. × clermontiae Syme
        A. ruta-muraria × septentrionale = A. × murbeckii
          Dörfl.
    8 A. septentrionale (L.) Hoffm.
        A. septentrionale × trichomanes = A. × alternifolium
          Wulf.
        A. germanicum auct.; *A. breynii* auct.

ASPLENIUM × PHYLLITIS = × ASPLENOPHYLLITIS Alston
    A. adiantum-nigrum × P. scolopendrium = × Aspleno-
      phyllitis jacksonii Alston

A. obovatum×P. scolopendrium = × Asplenophyllitis
microdon (T. Moore) Alston
A. trichomanes × P. scolopendrium = × Asplenophyllitis confluens (Lowe) Alston

16 CETERACH DC.

1 C. officinarum DC.
Asplenium ceterach L.; *Ceterach ceterach* (L.) Newm.

ATHYRIACEAE

17 *MATTEUCCIA Tod.

1 *M. struthiopteris (L.) Tod.

18 ATHYRIUM Roth

1 A. filix-femina (L.) Roth
Asplenium filix-femina (L.) Bernh.
2 A. alpestre (Hoppe) Rylands *sensu lato*
Polypodium alpestre (Hoppe) Spenn.

1 A. alpestre (Hoppe) Rylands
Polypodium molle All., non Schreb.
2 A. flexile (Newm.) Druce
Polypodium flexile (Newm.) T. Moore, non Fée;
Athyrium alpestre var. *flexile* (Newm.) Druce

19 CYSTOPTERIS Bernh.

1 C. fragilis (L.) Bernh.
C. dentata (Sm.) Desv.; *C. regia* (L.) Desv.; *C. alpina*
(Roth) Desv.
2 C. dickieana Sim
3 C. montana (Lam.) Desv.

20 WOODSIA R. Br.

1 W. ilvensis (L.) R. Br.
2 W. alpina (Bolton) Gray

ASPIDIACEAE

21 DRYOPTERIS Adans.
Nephrodium Michx.

1 D. filix-mas (L.) Schott
Aspidium filix-mas (L.) Sw.; *Nephrodium filix-mas*
(L.) Strempel; *Lastrea filix-mas* (L.) C. Presl

4

    D. filix-mas × lanceolatocristata
     D. remota Druce *pro parte*; *Aspidium remotum* auct.;
     Lastrea remota auct.

2 D. borreri Newm.
    D. borreri × filix-mas = D. × tavelii Rothm.
    D. borreri × dilatata = D. × woynarii Rothm.

3 D. abbreviata (DC.) Newm.

4 D. villarii (Bellardi) Woynar
    Aspidium rigidum Sw.; *Nephrodium rigidum* (Sw.)
     Desv.; *Lastrea rigida* (Sw.) C. Presl

5 D. cristata (L.) A. Gray
    Aspidium cristatum (L.) Sw.; *Nephrodium cristatum*
     Michx.; *Lastrea cristata* (L.) C. Presl
    D. cristata × lanceolatocristata = D. × uliginosa(Newm.)
     Kuntze ex Druce
    Lastrea uliginosa Newm.

6 D. lanceolatocristata (Hoffm.) Alston
    Aspidium spinulosum Sw.; *Nephrodium spinulosum*
     Strempel; *Lastrea spinulosa* C. Presl; *Dryopteris*
     spinulosa Watt

7 D. dilatata (Hoffm.) A. Gray
    Aspidium dilatatum (Hoffm.) Sm.; *Nephrodium*
     dilatatum (Hoffm.) Desv.; *Lastrea dilatata* (Hoffm.)
     C. Presl; *L. aristata* Britten & Rendle, non T. Moore;
     Dryopteris aristata Druce, non Kuntze; *D. austriaca*
     auct.
    D. dilatata × filix-mas = D. × subaustriaca Rothm.
    D. dilatata × lanceolatocristata = D. × deweveri (Jansen)
     Jansen & Wachter.

8 D. aemula (Ait.) Kuntze
    Aspidium aemulum (Ait.) Sw.; *Lastrea aemula* (Ait.)
     Brackenr.; *Nephrodium aemulum* (Ait.) Bak.

22 POLYSTICHUM Roth

1 P. setiferum (Forsk.) Woynar
    Aspidium angulare Kit. ex Willd.; *Polystichum*
     angulare (Willd.) C. Presl; *P. braunii* auct.

2 P. aculeatum (L.) Roth
    Aspidium aculeatum (L.) Sw.; *A. lobatum* (Huds.)
     Sw.; *Polystichum lobatum* (Huds.) Chevall.
    P. aculeatum × setiferum = P. × bicknellii (Christ) Hahne

3   P. lonchitis (L.) Roth
    Aspidium lonchitis (L.) Sw.

23 *CYRTOMIUM C. Presl
1   *C. falcatum (L. f.) C. Presl

THELYPTERIDACEAE

24 THELYPTERIS Schmidel
Lastrea Bory; *Gymnocarpium* Newm.; *Phegopteris* (C. Presl) Fée
1   T. oreopteris (Ehrh.) Slosson
    Aspidium oreopteris (Ehrh.) Sw.; *Lastrea oreopteris* (Ehrh.) Bory; *Nephrodium oreopteris* (Ehrh.) Desv.; *Lastrea montana* Newm.; *Dryopteris oreopteris* (Ehrh.) Maxon
2   T. palustris Schott
    Aspidium thelypteris (L.) Sw.; *Nephrodium thelypteris* (L.) Strempel; *Lastrea thelypteris* (L.) Bory; *Dryopteris thelypteris* (L.) A. Gray
3   T. phegopteris (L.) Slosson
    Polypodium phegopteris L.; *Phegopteris polypodioides* Fée; *Dryopteris phegopteris* (L.) C. Chr.
4   T. dryopteris (L.) Slosson
    Polypodium dryopteris L.; *Gymnocarpium dryopteris* (L.) Newm.; *Phegopteris dryopteris* (L.) Fée; *Dryopteris dryopteris* (L.) Christ
5   T. robertiana (Hoffm.) Slosson
    Polypodium robertianum Hoffm.; *Gymnocarpium robertianum* (Hoffm.) Newm.; *Phegopteris robertiana* (Hoffm.) A. Braun; *Dryopteris robertiana* (Hoffm.) C. Chr.

POLYPODIACEAE

25 POLYPODIUM L.
1   P. vulgare L.

MARSILEACEAE

26 PILULARIA L.
1   P. globulifera L.

*AZOLLACEAE

27 *AZOLLA Lam.
1 *A. filiculoides Lam.

OPHIOGLOSSACEAE

28 BOTRYCHIUM Sw.
1 B. lunaria (L.) Sw.
2 ‡B. lanceolatum (S. G. Gmel.) Ångstr.
3 ‡B. matricariifolium A. Braun ex Koch
B. *multifidum* auct.
4 ‡B. multifidum (S. G. Gmel.) Rupr.
B. *matricariae* (Schrank) Spreng.

29 OPHIOGLOSSUM L.
1 O. vulgatum L.
a subsp. vulgatum
b subsp. ambiguum (Coss. & Germ.) E. F. Warb.
O. *vulgatum* subsp. *polyphyllum* E. F. Warb. *pro parte*
2 O. lusitanicum L.

SPERMATOPHYTA

GYMNOSPERMAE

PINACEAE

30 *PSEUDOTSUGA* Carrière
1 *P. menziesii (Mirb.) Franco
P. *taxifolia* Britton

31 *PICEA* A. Dietr.
1 *P. abies (L.) Karst.
Abies abies (L.) Rusby
2 *P. sitchensis (Bong.) Carrière

32 *LARIX* Mill.
1 *L. decidua Mill.
L. *larix* (L.) Karst.

33 PINUS L.
1 P. sylvestris L.
2 *P. pinaster Ait.

7

CUPRESSACEAE

34 JUNIPERUS L.
  1 J. communis L.
    a subsp. communis
    b subsp. nana Syme
      J. sibirica Burgsd.; *J. nana* Willd.

TAXACEAE

35 TAXUS L.
  1 T. baccata L.

ANGIOSPERMAE
DICOTYLEDONES
RANUNCULACEAE

36 CALTHA L.
  1 C. palustris L.
    C. radicans auct.

37 TROLLIUS L.
  1 T. europaeus L.

38 HELLEBORUS L.
  1 H. foetidus L.
  2 H. viridis L.
    subsp. occidentalis (Reut.) Schiffn.

39 *ERANTHIS Salisb.
    Cammarum Hill
  1 *E. hyemalis (L.) Salisb.
    Cammarum hyemale (L.) Greene

40 ACONITUM L.
  1 A. napellus L. *sensu lato*
    1 A. anglicum Stapf
    2 *A. compactum (Reichb.) Gáyer

41 *DELPHINIUM L.
  1 *D. ambiguum L.
    D. gayanum Wilmott; *D. ajacis* auct.

RANUNCULACEAE

42 ACTAEA L.
    1 A. spicata L.

43 ANEMONE L.
    1 A. nemorosa L.
    2 *A. ranunculoides L.
    3 *A. apennina L.

44 PULSATILLA Mill.
    1 P. vulgaris Mill.
        Anemone pulsatilla L.

45 CLEMATIS L.
    1 C. vitalba L.
    2 *C. flammula L.
    3 *C. montana Buch.-Ham. ex DC.
    4 *C. viticella L.

46 RANUNCULUS L.
    1 R. acris L.
    2 R. repens L.
    3 R. bulbosus L.
        R. aleae auct.
    4 [R. paludosus Poir.
        R. flabellatus Desf.; *R. chaerophyllos* auct.]
    5 R. arvensis L.
    6 *R. muricatus L.
    7 R. sardous Crantz
        R. hirsutus Curt.
    8 *R. marginatus D'Urv.
        *subsp. trachycarpus (Fisch. & Mey.) Hayek
          R. trachycarpus Fisch. & Mey.
    9 R. parviflorus L.
  10 R. auricomus L.
  11 R. lingua L.
  12 R. flammula L.
      a subsp. flammula
      b subsp. scoticus (E. S. Marshall) Clapham
        R. scoticus E. S. Marshall
      c subsp. minimus (A. Benn.) Padmore
      R. flammula × reptans

13 ‡R. reptans L.
14 R. ophioglossifolius Vill.
15 R. sceleratus L.
16 R. hederaceus L.
17 R. lenormandii F. W. Schultz
    R. omiophyllus auct.
18 R. tripartitus DC.
    R. lutarius (Revel) Bouvet
19 R. fluitans Lam.
20 R. circinatus Sibth.
    R. divaricatus auct.
21 R. trichophyllus Chaix
  a   subsp. trichophyllus
  b   subsp. drouetii (Godr.) Clapham
      R. drouetii F. W. Schultz ex Godr.; *R. paucista-*
      mineus auct.
22 R. aquatilis L.
  a   subsp. aquatilis
      R. heterophyllus Weber; *R. radians* Revel
  b   subsp. peltatus (Schrank) Syme
      R. peltatus Schrank; *R. floribundus* Bab.; *R.*
      sphaerospermus auct.
  c   subsp. pseudofluitans (Syme) Clapham
      R. pseudofluitans (Syme) Newbould ex Bak. &
      Foggitt; *R. penicillatus* (Dumort.) Bab.
    R. aquatilis × lenormandii = R. × hiltonii H. & J. Groves
23 R. baudotii Godr.
    R. marinus (Fr.) Hartm.; *R. confusus* Godr.; *R.*
    obtusiflorus Moss *pro parte*
24 R. ficaria L.

47 *ADONIS L.

  1 *A. annua L.
    A. autumnalis L.

48 MYOSURUS L.

  1 M. minimus L.

49 AQUILEGIA L.

  1 A. vulgaris L.
  2 *A. pyrenaica DC.
    A. alpina auct.

50 THALICTRUM L.

1   T. flavum L.
2   T. alpinum L.
3   T. minus L.
   a   subsp. minus
         T. montanum Wallr.; *T. babingtonii* Butcher; *T.
         collinum* auct.
   b   subsp. arenarium (Butcher) Clapham
         T. marinum Druce; *T. arenarium* Butcher; *T.
         dunense* auct.
   c   subsp. majus (Crantz) Clapham
         T. majus Crantz; *T. capillare* Reichb.; *T. kochii*
         Fr.; *T. expansum* Jord.; *T. umbrosum* Butcher

*PAEONIACEAE

51 *PAEONIA L.

1   *P. mascula (L.) Mill.
    P. corallina Retz.; *P. officinalis* auct.

BERBERIDACEAE

52 *EPIMEDIUM L.

1   *E. alpinum L.

53 BERBERIS L.

1   B. vulgaris L.
2   *B. glaucocarpa Stapf
    B. aristata auct.
3   *B. buxifolia Pers.

54 *MAHONIA Nutt.

1   *M. aquifolium (Pursh) Nutt.
    Berberis aquifolium Pursh

NYMPHAEACEAE

55 NYMPHAEA L.
   Castalia Salisb.

1   N. alba L.
    Castalia alba (L.) Wood; *Nymphaea occidentalis*
    (Ostenf.) Moss

11

56 NUPHAR Sm.
> 1 N. lutea (L.) Sm.
> *Nymphaea lutea* L.
> N. lutea×pumila=N.×spennerana Gaudin
> *N. intermedia* Ledeb.
> 2 N. pumila (Timm) DC.
> *Nymphaea pumila* (Timm) Hoffm.

CERATOPHYLLACEAE

57 CERATOPHYLLUM L.
> 1 C. demersum L.
> 2 C. submersum L.

PAPAVERACEAE

58 PAPAVER L.
> 1 P. rhoeas L.
> 2 P. dubium L.
> 3 P. lecoqii Lamotte
> 4 P. hybridum L.
> 5 P. argemone L.
> 6 *P. somniferum L.
> 7 *P. lateritium C. Koch
> 8 *P. atlanticum (Ball) Coss.

59 MECONOPSIS Vig.
> 1 M. cambrica (L.) Vig.

60 *ROEMERIA Medic.
> 1 *R. hybrida (L.) DC.

61 GLAUCIUM Mill.
> 1 G. flavum Crantz
> *G. luteum* Crantz; *G. glaucium* (L.) Karst.

62 CHELIDONIUM L.
> 1 C. majus L.
> *C. laciniatum* Mill.

63 *ESCHSCHOLZIA Cham.
> 1 *E. californica Cham.
> *E. douglasii* (Hook. & Arn.) Walp.

12

FUMARIACEAE

FUMARIACEAE

64 *DICENTRA Bernh.
Capnorchis Mill.

  1 *D. spectabilis (L.) Lemaire
    Capnorchis spectabilis (L.) Borkh.

65 CORYDALIS Medic.
Capnoides Mill.

  1 *C. solida (L.) Sw.
    Capnoides solida (L.) Moench; *Corydalis bulbosa* auct.
  2 *C. bulbosa (L.) DC.
    C. cava (L.) Schweigg. & Koerte; *Capnoides bulbosa* (L.) Druce
  3 C. claviculata (L.) DC.
    Capnoides claviculata (L.) Kuntze
  4 *C. lutea (L.) DC.
    Capnoides lutea (L.) Gaertn.

66 FUMARIA L.
  1 F. occidentalis Pugsl.
  2 F. capreolata L.
    F. speciosa Jord.
  3 F. purpurea Pugsl.
  4 F. bastardii Bor.
    F. bastardii × muralis
  5 F. martinii Clavaud
    F. paradoxa Pugsl.
  6 F. muralis Sond. ex Koch
  a subsp. muralis
  b subsp. boraei (Jord.) Pugsl.
    F. boraei Jord.
  c subsp. neglecta Pugsl.
    F. neglecta (Pugsl.) Pugsl.
    F. muralis × officinalis=F. × painteri Pugsl.
  7 F. micrantha Lag.
    F. densiflora auct.
    F. micrantha × officinalis
  8 F. officinalis L.
    F. officinalis × vaillantii=F. × albertii Rouy & Fouc.
    F. officinalis × parviflora
  9 F. vaillantii Lois.
 10 F. parviflora Lam.

13

CRUCIFERAE

67 BRASSICA L.

    1   B. oleracea L.

    2 *B. napus L.
         B. napobrassica (L.) Mill.; *B. rutabaga* (DC.) Briggs

    3 *B. rapa L.
         B. campestris L.

    4   B. nigra (L.) Koch
         Sinapis nigra L.

68 *ERUCASTRUM C. Presl

    1 *E. gallicum (Willd.) O. E. Schulz
         Brassica gallica (Willd.) Druce

69 RHYNCHOSINAPIS Hayek
    Brassicella Fourr. ex O. E. Schulz

    1   R. monensis (L.) Dandy
         Brassica monensis (L.) Huds.; *Brassicella monensis* (L.) O. E. Schulz

    2   R. wrightii (O. E. Schulz) Dandy
         Brassicella wrightii O. E. Schulz

    3 *R. cheiranthos (Vill.) Dandy
         Brassica cheiranthos Vill.; *Rhynchosinapis erucastrum* Dandy *pro parte*; *Brassicella erucastrum* auct.

70 SINAPIS L.

    1   S. arvensis L.
         Brassica arvensis (L.) Rabenh., non L.; *B. sinapis* Vis.; *B. kaber* (DC.) L. C. Wheeler

    2 *S. alba L.
         Brassica alba (L.) Rabenh.

71 [*HIRSCHFELDIA Moench]

    1 [*H. incana (L.) Lagr.-Foss.
         Sinapis incana L.; *Brassica adpressa* Boiss.; *B. incana* (L.) Meigen, non Ten.]

72 DIPLOTAXIS DC.

    1 *D. muralis (L.) DC.
         Brassica muralis (L.) Huds.

2 D. tenuifolia (L.) DC.
     Brassica tenuifolia (L.) Fr.
3 *D. erucoides (L.) DC.

73 *ERUCA Mill.
  1 *E. sativa Mill.
      E. cappadocica Reut. ex Boiss.; *E. eruca* (L.) Aschers.
      & Graebn.

74 RAPHANUS L.
  1 R. raphanistrum L.
  2 R. maritimus Sm.
  3 *R. sativus L.

75 CRAMBE L.
  1 C. maritima L.

76 *RAPISTRUM Crantz
  1 *R. perenne (L.) All.
  2 *R. rugosum (L.) All.
  3 *R. orientale (L.) Crantz
      R. rugosum subsp. *orientale* (L.) Rouy & Fouc.

77 CAKILE Mill.
  1 C. maritima Scop.
      C. cakile (L.) Karst.
  a subsp. maritima
  b subsp. integrifolia (Hornem.) Hyland.
      C. edentula auct.

78 *CONRINGIA Adans.
  1 *C. orientalis (L.) Dumort.
      Erysimum orientale (L.) Crantz, non Mill.

79 LEPIDIUM L.
  1 *L. sativum L.
  2 L. campestre (L.) R. Br.
  3 L. heterophyllum Benth.
      L. hirtum Sm. *pro parte*; *L. smithii* Hook.
  4 *L. ruderale L.
  5 *L. neglectum Thell.
  6 L. latifolium L.
  7 *L. graminifolium L.

80 CORONOPUS Zinn
 Senebiera DC.

    1 C. squamatus (Forsk.) Aschers.
        C. procumbens Gilib.; *C. ruellii* All.; *Senebiera*
        coronopus (L.) Poir.; *Coronopus coronopus* (L.)
        Karst.
    2 *C. didymus (L.) Sm.
        Senebiera didyma (L.) Pers.

81 *CARDARIA Desv.

    1 *C. draba (L.) Desv.
        Lepidium draba L.
    2 *C. chalepensis (L.) Hand.-Mazz.
        Lepidium chalepense L.

82 *ISATIS L.

    1 *I. tinctoria L.

83 IBERIS L.

    1 I. amara L.

84 THLASPI L.

    1 T. arvense L.
    2 *T. alliaceum L.
    3 T. perfoliatum L.
    4 T. alpestre L.
        T. virens auct.; *T. calaminare* auct.

85 TEESDALIA R. Br.

    1 T. nudicaulis (L.) R. Br.
    2 ‡T. coronopifolia (Bergeret) Thell.

86 CAPSELLA Medic.
 Bursa Boehm.

    1 C. bursa-pastoris (L.) Medic.
        Bursa pastoris Weber[1]; *B. penarthae* Shull; *Capsella*
        penarthae (Shull) Wilmott
    2 *C. rubella Reut.

[1] Together with 27 names of microspecies listed under *Bursa* by Druce in the *British Plant List* (ed. 2), 10, spp. 2–28.

CRUCIFERAE

87 HORNUNGIA Reichb.
    1 H. petraea (L.) Reichb.
        Hutchinsia petraea (L.) R. Br.

88 COCHLEARIA L.
    1 C. officinalis L.
    2 C. alpina (Bab.) H. C. Wats.
    3 C. micacea E. S. Marshall
    4 C. scotica Druce
        C. groenlandica auct.
    5 C. danica L.
        C. danica × officinalis
    6 C. anglica L.
        C. anglica × officinalis = C. × hollandica Henrard

89 SUBULARIA L.
    1 S. aquatica L.

90 *BUNIAS L.
    1 *B. erucago L.
    2 *B. orientalis L.

91 *ALYSSUM L.
    1 *A. alyssoides (L.) L.
        A. calycinum L.

92 *LOBULARIA Desv.
    1 *L. maritima (L.) Desv.
        Alyssum maritimum (L.) Lam.

93 *BERTEROA DC.
    1 *B. incana (L.) DC.
        Alyssum incanum L.

94 DRABA L.
    1 D. aizoides L.
    2 D. norvegica Gunn.
        D. rupestris R. Br.; *D. hirta* auct.
    3 D. incana L.
    4 D. muralis L.

CRUCIFERAE

95 EROPHILA DC.

    1 E. verna (L.) Chevall.
        Draba verna L.; *Erophila vulgaris* DC.; *E. oedocarpa* Drabble

    2 E. spathulata Láng
        E. boerhaavii (Van Hall) Dumort.; *Draba inflata* (Bab.) H. C. Wats.; *Erophila inflata* (Bab.) F. J. Hanb.

    3 E. praecox (Stev.) DC.
        Draba praecox Stev.

96 *ARMORACIA Gilib.

    1 *A. rusticana Gaertn., Mey. & Scherb.
        Cochlearia armoracia L.; *Armoracia lapathifolia* Gilib.

97 CARDAMINE L.
    Dentaria L.

    1 C. pratensis L.
    2 C. amara L.
    3 C. impatiens L.
    4 C. flexuosa With.
        C. flexuosa × pratensis = C. × haussknechtiana O. E. Schulz
    5 C. hirsuta L.
    6 *C. trifolia L.
    7 *C. latifolia Vahl
    8 C. bulbifera (L.) Crantz
        Dentaria bulbifera L.

98 BARBAREA R. Br.

    1 B. vulgaris R. Br.
        B. arcuata (J. & C. Presl) Reichb.; *B. lyrata* Aschers.; *B. barbarea* (L.) MacMill.

    2 B. stricta Andrz.
    3 *B. intermedia Bor.
        B. sicula auct.
    4 *B. verna (Mill.) Aschers.
        B. praecox (Sm.) R. Br.

99 CARDAMINOPSIS (C. A. Mey.) Hayek

    1 C. petraea (L.) Hiit.
        Arabis petraea (L.) Lam.

CRUCIFERAE

100 ARABIS L.

    1 *A. turrita L.
    2 A. alpina L.
    3 *A. caucasica Willd.
    4 A. hirsuta (L.) Scop.
    5 A. brownii Jord.
        A. hibernica Wilmott; *A. ciliata* auct.
        A. brownii × hirsuta
    6 A. stricta Huds.
        A. scabra All.

101 TURRITIS L.

    1 T. glabra L.
        Arabis perfoliata Lam.; *A. glabra* (L.) Bernh.

102 RORIPPA Scop.

    Radicula Moench; *Nasturtium* R. Br.

    1 R. nasturtium-aquaticum (L.) Hayek
        Nasturtium officinale R. Br.; *Radicula nasturtium-
         aquaticum* (L.) Druce
    2 R. microphylla (Boenn.) Hyland.
        Nasturtium microphyllum (Boenn.) Reichb.; *N. uni-
        seriatum* Howard & Manton
        R. microphylla × nasturtium-aquaticum = R. × sterilis
        Airy Shaw
    3 R. sylvestris (L.) Bess.
        Nasturtium sylvestre (L.) R. Br.; *Radicula sylvestris*
        (L.) Druce
    4 R. islandica (Oeder) Borbás
        Radicula palustris (L.) Moench; *Nasturtium palustre*
        (L.) DC., non Crantz; *Radicula islandica* (Oeder)
        Druce
    5 R. amphibia (L.) Bess.
        Nasturtium amphibium (L.) R. Br.; *Armoracia am-
        phibia* (L.) G. F. W. Mey.; *Radicula amphibia* (L.)
        Druce
        R. amphibia × sylvestris
        Radicula barbaraeoides Druce
        R. amphibia × islandica = R. × erythrocaulis Borbás
        Radicula erythrocaulis (Borbás) Druce
    6 *R. austriaca (Crantz) Bess.
        Radicula austriaca (Crantz) Druce

19

103 MATTHIOLA R. Br.
  1   M. incana (L.) R. Br.
  2   M. sinuata (L.) R. Br.

104 *HESPERIS L.
  1   *H. matronalis L.

105 *ERYSIMUM L.
  1   *E. cheiranthoides L.

106 *CHEIRANTHUS L.
  1   *C. cheiri L.

107 ALLIARIA Scop.
  1   A. petiolata (Bieb.) Cavara & Grande
   Sisymbrium alliaria (L.) Scop.; *Alliaria officinalis*
   Andrz. ex Bieb.; *A. alliacea* Britten & Rendle

108 SISYMBRIUM L.
  1   S. officinale (L.) Scop.
  2   *S. irio L.
  3   *S. loeselii L.
  4   *S. orientale L.
   S. columnae Jacq.
  5   *S. altissimum L.
   S. sinapistrum Crantz; *S. pannonicum* Jacq.
  6   *S. strictissimum L.

109 ARABIDOPSIS (DC.) Heynh.
  1   A. thaliana (L.) Heynh.
   Arabis thaliana L.; *Sisymbrium thalianum* (L.) Gay

110 *CAMELINA Crantz
  1   *C. sativa (L.) Crantz
  2   *C. microcarpa Andrz. ex DC.
   C. sylvestris Wallr.

111 *DESCURAINIA Webb & Berth.
  1   *D. sophia (L.) Webb ex Prantl
   Sisymbrium sophia L.

RESEDACEAE

112 RESEDA L.

1 R. luteola L.
2 R. lutea L.
   R. stricta auct.
3 *R. alba L.
4 *R. phyteuma L.

VIOLACEAE

113 VIOLA L.

1 V. odorata L.
2 V. hirta L.
  a   subsp. hirta
  b   subsp. calcarea (Bab.) E. F. Warb.
        V. calcarea (Bab.) Gregory
  V. hirta × odorata = V. × permixta Jord.
    V. multicaulis Jord.; *V. gigas* (Gregory) Druce; *V. collina* auct.; *V. sepincola* auct.
3 V. rupestris Schmidt
    V. arenaria DC.
4 V. riviniana Reichb.
  a   subsp. riviniana
  b   subsp. minor (Gregory) Valentine
  V. riviniana × rupestris = V. × burnatii Gremli
5 V. reichenbachiana Jord. ex Bor.
    V. sylvestris auct.
  V. reichenbachiana × riviniana
    V. intermedia Reichb., non Krock.
6 V. canina L.
  a   subsp. canina
  b   subsp. montana (L.) Hartm.
        V. montana L.; *V. ruppii* All.
  V. canina × riviniana
  V. canina × lactea = V. × militaris Savouré
    V. intermedia H. C. Wats., non Krock.; *V. pumiliformis* (Rouy & Fouc.) Gregory
  V. canina × stagnina = V. × ritschliana W. Becker
7 V. lactea Sm.
  V. lactea × riviniana
8 V. stagnina Kit.
    V. persicifolia auct.

21

9 V. palustris L.
   a   subsp. palustris
       V. ruprechtiana auct.
   b   subsp. juressi (Neves) P. Fourn.
       V. juressi Link ex Neves; *V. epipsila* auct.

10 *V. cornuta L.
11 V. lutea Huds.
      V. lutea × tricolor
12 V. tricolor L.
   a   subsp. tricolor
       V. cantiana Drabble; *V. orcadensis* Drabble;
       V. lejeunii auct.; *V. lloydii* auct.; *V. lepida*
       auct.; *V. pesneaui* auct.; *V. tricolor* subsp.
       saxatilis auct.
   b   subsp. curtisii (E. Forst.) Syme
       V. curtisii E. Forst.
13 V. arvensis Murr.
      V. latifolia Drabble; *V. anglica* Drabble; *V. agrestis*
      auct.; *V. segetalis* auct.; *V. obtusifolia* auct.;
      V. ruralis auct.; *V. deseglisei* auct.; *V. arvatica*
      auct.; *V. derelicta* auct.
    V. arvensis × tricolor
      V. contempta auct.; *V. variata* auct.; *V. monticola*
      auct.; *V. alpestris* auct.; ? *V. vectensis* (F. N.
      Williams) Drabble
14 V. kitaibeliana Schult.
    V. nana (DC.) Godr.

POLYGALACEAE

114 POLYGALA L.

1 P. vulgaris L.
    P. oxyptera Reichb.; *P. dubia* Bellynck; *P. babing-*
    tonii Druce
2 P. serpyllifolia Hose
    P. serpyllacea Weihe; *P. depressa* Wender.
3 P. calcarea F. W. Schultz
    P. calcarea × vulgaris
4 P. amara L. *sensu lato*

   1   P. amara L.
       P. amarella Crantz
   2   P. austriaca Crantz

GUTTIFERAE

115 HYPERICUM L.

  1 H. androsaemum L.
  2 *H. elatum Ait.
      H. grandifolium Choisy
  3 *H. hircinum L.
  4 *H. calycinum L.
  5 H. perforatum L.
  6 H. maculatum Crantz
      H. dubium Leers; *H. quadrangulum* auct.
     a   subsp. maculatum
     b   subsp. obtusiusculum (Tourlet) Hayek
      H. maculatum×perforatum=H.×desetangsii Lamotte
  7 H. undulatum Schousb. ex Willd.
  8 H. tetrapterum Fr.
      H. quadrangulum L., *nom. ambig.*; *H. acutum*
        Moench; *H. quadratum* Stokes
  9 H. humifusum L.
 10 H. linarifolium Vahl
 11 H. pulchrum L.
 12 H. hirsutum L.
 13 H. montanum L.
 14 H. elodes L.
 15 H. canadense L.

*PITTOSPORACEAE

116 *PITTOSPORUM Banks ex Soland.

  1 *P. crassifolium Soland. ex Putterl.

CISTACEAE

117 TUBERARIA (Dunal) Spach

  1 T. guttata (L.) Fourr.
      Helianthemum guttatum (L.) Mill.
     a   subsp. guttata
     b   subsp. breweri (Planch.) E. F. Warb.
        Helianthemum guttatum subsp. *breweri* (Planch.)
        Syme

118 HELIANTHEMUM Mill.

  1 H. chamaecistus Mill.
      H. vulgare Gaertn.; *H. helianthemum* (L.) Karst.;
      H. bickhami E. S. Marshall; *H. nummularium*
      auct.
  2 H. apenninum (L.) Mill.
      H. polifolium Mill.
      H. apenninum × chamaecistus = H. × sulphureum
      Willd.
  3 H. canum (L.) Baumg.
    a subsp. canum
        H. marifolium Mill.
    b subsp. levigatum M. C. F. Proctor

119 *CISTUS L.

  1 *C. incanus L.

*TAMARICACEAE

120 *TAMARIX L.

  1 *T. anglica Webb
  2 *T. gallica L.

FRANKENIACEAE

121 FRANKENIA L.

  1 F. laevis L.

ELATINACEAE

122 ELATINE L.

  1 E. hexandra (Lapierre) DC.
  2 E. hydropiper L.

CARYOPHYLLACEAE

123 SILENE L.
    Melandrium Röhl.

  1 S. vulgaris (Moench) Garcke
      S. cucubalus Wibel
    a subsp. vulgaris
        S. angustifolia (DC.) Guss., non Poir.; *S.*
          latifolia (Mill.) Britten & Rendle, non Poir.
    b *subsp. macrocarpa Turrill
        S. angustifolia auct.

2 S. maritima With.
   S. maritima × vulgaris
3 S. conica L.
4 [*S. conoidea L.]
5 *S. dichotoma Ehrh.
6 S. gallica L.
   S. anglica L.; *S. quinquevulnera* L.
7 S. acaulis (L.) Jacq.
8 *S. armeria L.
9 S. otites (L.) Wibel
10 S. nutans L.
   S. dubia Herbich
11 *S. italica (L.) Pers.
12 S. noctiflora L.
   Melandrium noctiflorum (L.) Fr.
13 S. dioica (L.) Clairv.
   Lychnis dioica L.; *L. diurna* Sibth.; *Melandrium dioicum* (L.) Coss. & Germ.; *M. rubrum* (Weigel) Garcke
14 S. alba (Mill.) E. H. L. Krause
   Lychnis alba Mill.; *L. vespertina* Sibth.; *Melandrium album* (Mill.) Garcke
   S. alba × dioica
   Lychnis intermedia (Schur) Druce

124 LYCHNIS L.
   Viscaria Bernh.

1 L. alpina L.
   Viscaria alpina (L.) G. Don
2 L. viscaria L.
   Viscaria vulgaris Bernh.
3 L. flos-cuculi L.

125 *AGROSTEMMA L.
   Githago Adans.

1 *A. githago L.
   Lychnis githago (L.) Scop.; *Githago segetum* Link

126 *CUCUBALUS L.
1 *C. baccifer L.

127 DIANTHUS L.
1 D. armeria L.
2 *D. barbatus L.

25

3 *D. carthusianorum L.
4 *D. plumarius L.
5 *D. caryophyllus L.
6 [*D. gallicus Pers.]
7 D. gratianopolitanus Vill.
   D. caesius Sm.
8 D. deltoides L.

128 *VACCARIA Medic.
   1 *V. pyramidata Medic.
      Saponaria vaccaria L.

129 SAPONARIA L.
   1 S. officinalis L.

130 KOHLRAUSCHIA Kunth
   1 K. prolifera (L.) Kunth
      Dianthus prolifer L.; *Tunica prolifera* (L.) Scop.
   2 *K. saxifraga (L.) Dandy
      Tunica saxifraga (L.) Scop.

131 CERASTIUM L.
   1 C. cerastoides (L.) Britton
      C. trigynum Vill.
   2 C. arvense L.
   3 *C. tomentosum L.
   4 C. alpinum L.
      C. alpinum × arcticum = C. × blyttii Baenitz
      C. alpinum × holosteoides = C. × symei Druce
      C. laestadianum auct.
   5 C. arcticum Lange
      C. nigrescens auct.; *C. edmondstonii* auct.
      C. arcticum × holosteoides = C. × richardsonii Druce
   6 C. nigrescens Edmondst. ex H. C. Wats.
      C. edmondstonii (Edmondst.) Murb. & Ostenf.
   7 C. holosteoides Fr.
      C. vulgatum auct.
   8 C. glomeratum Thuill.
      C. viscosum auct.
   9 C. brachypetalum Pers.

CARYOPHYLLACEAE

10 C. atrovirens Bab.
  C. tetrandrum Curt.; *C. subtetrandrum* auct.
11 C. pumilum Curt.
12 C. semidecandrum L.

132 MYOSOTON Moench

1 M. aquaticum (L.) Moench
  Stellaria aquatica (L.) Scop.

133 STELLARIA L.

1 S. nemorum L.
  a   subsp. nemorum
  b   subsp. glochidisperma Murb.
2 S. media (L.) Vill.
3 S. pallida (Dumort.) Piré
  S. boraeana Jord.; *S. apetala* auct.
4 S. neglecta Weihe
  S. umbrosa Opiz; *S. elisabethae* F. W. Schultz
5 S. holostea L.
6 S. palustris Retz.
  S. dilleniana Moench, non Leers; *S. glauca* With.
7 S. graminea L.
8 S. alsine Grimm
  S. uliginosa Murr.

134 †HOLOSTEUM L.

1 †H. umbellatum L.

135 MOENCHIA Ehrh.

1 M. erecta (L.) Gaertn., Mey. & Scherb.
  Cerastium quaternellum Fenzl; *C. erectum* (L.)
  Coss. & Germ.

136 SAGINA L.

1 S. apetala Ard.
2 S. ciliata Fr.
  S. filicaulis Jord.; *S. reuteri* auct.
3 S. maritima Don
4 S. procumbens L.
  S. procumbens × subulata = S. × micrantha Bor. ex
  É. Martin

CARYOPHYLLACEAE

5 ‡S. boydii F. B. White
6 S. saginoides (L.) Karst.
   S. linnei C. Presl
7 S. normaniana Lagerh.
   S. scotica (Druce) Druce; *S. saginoides* subsp.
   scotica (Druce) Clapham
8 S. intermedia Fenzl
   S. nivalis auct.; *S. caespitosa* auct.
9 S. subulata (Sw.) C. Presl
10 S. nodosa (L.) Fenzl

137 MINUARTIA L.

1 M. verna (L.) Hiern
   Arenaria verna L.; *A. gerardi* Willd.; *Alsine verna*
   (L.) Wahlenb.; *Minuartia gerardi* (Willd.) Hayek
2 M. rubella (Wahlenb.) Hiern
   Alsine rubella Wahlenb.; *Arenaria sulcata* Willd. ex
   Schlecht.; *A. hirta* Wormsk. ex Hornem.; *A.
   rubella* (Wahlenb.) Sm.
3 M. stricta (Sw.) Hiern
   Arenaria uliginosa Schleich. ex DC.; *Alsine stricta*
   (Sw.) Wahlenb.
4 M. hybrida (Vill.) Schischk.
   Arenaria tenuifolia L.; *Alsine tenuifolia* (L.) Crantz;
   Minuartia tenuifolia (L.) Hiern, non Nees ex Mart.

138 CHERLERIA L.

1 C. sedoides L.
   Arenaria cherleria (Peterm.) Ardoino; *A. sedoides*
   (L.) F. J. Hanb.

139 HONKENYA Ehrh.

1 H. peploides (L.) Ehrh.
   Arenaria peploides L.

140 MOEHRINGIA L.

1 M. trinervia (L.) Clairv.
   Arenaria trinervia L.

141 ARENARIA L.

1 A. serpyllifolia L.
2 A. leptoclados (Reichb.) Guss.
3 A. ciliata L.
   subsp. hibernica Ostenf. & Dahl

28

4   A. norvegica Gunn.
5   A. gothica Fr.
6   *A. balearica L.
7   *A. montana L.

142 SPERGULA L.
1   S. arvensis L.
    S. sativa Boenn.; *S. vulgaris* Boenn.
2   *S. morisonii Bor.
    S. pentandra auct.; *S. vernalis* auct.

143 SPERGULARIA (Pers.) J. & C. Presl
1   S. rubra (L.) J. & C. Presl
    Alsine rubra (L.) Crantz
2   S. bocconii (Scheele) Aschers. & Graebn.
    S. campestris auct.
3   S. rupicola Lebel ex Le Jolis
    S. rupestris Lebel, non Cambess.; *Alsine rupicola*
    (Le Jolis) Hiern
4   S. media (L.) C. Presl
    Alsine marginata Reichb.; *Spergularia marginata*
    Kittel
5   S. marina (L.) Griseb.
    S. salina J. & C. Presl; *Alsine media* auct.
    S. marina × rupicola
    S. marina × media

144 POLYCARPON L.
1   P. tetraphyllum (L.) L.

ILLECEBRACEAE

145 CORRIGIOLA L.
1   C. litoralis L.

146 HERNIARIA L.
1   H. glabra L.
2   H. ciliolata Melderis
    H. ciliata Bab., non Clairv.
3   *H. hirsuta L.
4   *H. cinerea DC.

147 ILLECEBRUM L.
1   I. verticillatum L.

148 SCLERANTHUS L.

    1 S. annuus L. *sensu lato*

       1 S. annuus L.
       2 S. polycarpos L.

    2 S. perennis L.

PORTULACACEAE

149 MONTIA L.

    1 M. fontana L.

      a subsp. fontana
          M. lamprosperma Cham.

      b subsp. chondrosperma (Fenzl) Walters
          M. verna auct.

      c subsp. intermedia (Beeby) Walters
          M. lusitanica Samp.; *M. rivularis* auct.

      d subsp. variabilis Walters
          M. rivularis auct.

    2 *M. perfoliata (Willd.) Howell
        Claytonia perfoliata Donn ex Willd.

    3 *M. sibirica (L.) Howell
        Claytonia sibirica L.; *C. alsinoides* Sims

150 *CLAYTONIA L.

    1 *C. virginica L.

151 *PORTULACA L.

    1 *P. oleracea L.

*AIZOACEAE

152 *CARPOBROTUS N. E. Br.

    1 *C. edulis (L.) N. E. Br.

*AMARANTHACEAE

153 *AMARANTHUS L.

    1 *A. retroflexus L.
    2 *A. hybridus L.
        A. chlorostachys Willd.
    3 *A. albus L.
    4 *A. lividus L.
        A. blitum L.

CHENOPODIACEAE

154 CHENOPODIUM L.
 1 *C. bonus-henricus L.
 2 C. polyspermum L.
 3 C. vulvaria L.
 4 C. album L.
   C. reticulatum Aellen
   C. album × berlandieri = C. × variabile Aellen
   C. subcuneatum auct.
   C. album × opulifolium = C. × preissmannii J. Murr
   C. album × ficifolium = C. × zahnii J. Murr
 5 *C. suecicum J. Murr
   C. viride auct.
 6 *C. berlandieri Moq.
     *subsp. zschackei (J. Murr) Zobel
       C. zschackei J. Murr
 7 *C. opulifolium Schrad. ex Koch & Ziz
 8 *C. hircinum Schrad.
 9 C. ficifolium Sm.
10 *C. pratericola Rydb.
   C. leptophyllum auct.
11 C. murale L.
12 *C. urbicum L.
13 *C. hybridum L.
14 C. rubrum L.
15 C. botryodes Sm.
   C. crassifolium Hornem.
16 *C. glaucum L.
17 *C. capitatum (L.) Aschers.

155 BETA L.
 1 B. vulgaris L.
     subsp. maritima (L.) Thell.
       B. maritima L.
 2 *B. trigyna Waldst. & Kit.

156 ATRIPLEX L.
 1 A. littoralis L.
 2 A. patula L.
   A. erecta Huds.
 3 A. hastata L.
   A. deltoidea Bab.; *A. calotheca* auct.

31

4   A. glabriuscula Edmondst.
5   A. laciniata L.
      A. maritima L.; *A. arenaria* Woods, non Nutt.; *A. sabulosa* Rouy
6   *A. hortensis L.
7   *A. halimus L.

157 HALIMIONE Aellen
1   H. portulacoides (L.) Aellen
      Atriplex portulacoides L.; *Obione portulacoides* (L.) Moq.
†2   H. pedunculata (L.) Aellen
      Atriplex pedunculata L.; *Obione pedunculata* (L.) Moq.

158 SUAEDA Forsk. ex Scop.
   Dondia Adans.
1   S. maritima (L.) Dumort.
      Dondia maritima (L.) Druce
2   S. fruticosa Forsk.
      Dondia fruticosa (Forsk.) Druce

159 SALSOLA L.
1   S. kali L.
2   *S. pestifer A. Nels.
      S. tragus auct.

160 SALICORNIA L.
1   S. perennis Mill.
      S. radicans Sm.; *S. lignosa* Woods
2   S. dolichostachya Moss
3   S. europaea L.
      S. herbacea (L.) L.; *S. stricta* Dumort.
4   S. ramosissima Woods
      S. appressa Dumort.; *S. gracillima* (Townsend) Moss; *S. smithiana* Moss; *S. prostrata* auct.
5   S. pusilla Woods
      S. disarticulata Moss

*PHYTOLACCACEAE
161 *PHYTOLACCA L.
1   *P. americana L.

32

TILIACEAE
162 TILIA L.

    1 T. platyphyllos Scop.
    2 T. cordata Mill.
        T. parvifolia Ehrh. ex Hoffm.
    *T. cordata × platyphyllos = T. × europaea L.
        T. vulgaris Hayne

MALVACEAE
163 MALVA L.

    1 M. moschata L.
    2 M. sylvestris L.
    3 *M. nicaeensis All.
    4 M. neglecta Wallr.
        M. rotundifolia auct.
    5 *M. pusilla Sm.
        M. rotundifolia L., *nom. ambig.*
    6 *M. parviflora L.
    7 *M. verticillata L.

164 LAVATERA L.

    1 L. arborea L.
    2 L. cretica L.
        L. sylvestris Brot.

165 ALTHAEA L.

    1 A. officinalis L.
    2 *A. hirsuta L.

LINACEAE
166 LINUM L.

    1 L. bienne Mill.
        L. angustifolium Huds.
    2 *L. usitatissimum L.
    3 L. anglicum Mill.
        L. perenne auct.
    4 L. catharticum L.

167 RADIOLA Hill
    Millegrana Adans.
    1 R. linoides Roth
        R. radiola (L.) Karst.; *Millegrana radiola* (L.) Druce

33

GERANIACEAE

168 GERANIUM L.

1 G. pratense L.
2 G. sylvaticum L.
    G. angulatum Curt.
3 *G. endressii Gay
    *G. endressii × versicolor
4 *G. versicolor L.
    G. striatum L.
5 *G. nodosum L.
6 *G. phaeum L.
7 G. sanguineum L.
8 *G. macrorrhizum L.
9 G. pyrenaicum Burm. f.
    G. perenne Huds.
10 G. columbinum L.
11 G. dissectum L.
12 G. rotundifolium L.
13 G. molle L.
14 G. pusillum L.
15 G. lucidum L.
16 G. robertianum L.
   a   subsp. robertianum
   b   subsp. celticum Ostenf.
         G. robertianum var. *celticum* (Ostenf.) Druce
   c   subsp. maritimum (Bab.) H. G. Bak.
         G. robertianum var. *maritimum* Bab.
17 G. purpureum Vill.
   a   subsp. purpureum
   b   subsp. forsteri (Wilmott) H. G. Bak.

169 ERODIUM L'Hérit.

1 E. maritimum (L.) L'Hérit.
2 E. moschatum (L.) L'Hérit.
3 E. cicutarium (L.) L'Hérit.
   a   subsp. cicutarium
         E. pimpinellifolium (With.) Sibth.; *E. triviale*
         Jord.; *E. ballii* Jord.
   b   subsp. dunense Andreas
         E. lebeli Jord.; *E. neglectum* Bak. & Salmon
4 E. glutinosum Dumort.

34

OXALIDACEAE
170 OXALIS L.

   1 O. acetosella L.
   2 *O. corniculata L.
   3 *O. stricta L.
       O. dillenii Jacq.
   4 *O. europaea Jord.
       O. stricta auct.; *O. dillenii* auct.
   5 *O. megalorrhiza Jacq.
       O. carnosa auct.
   6 *O. articulata Savigny
       O. floribunda Lehm.; *O. rosea* auct.; *O. semiloba*
       auct.
   7 *O. corymbosa DC.
   8 *O. latifolia Kunth
   9 [*O. tetraphylla Cav.]
 10 *O. pes-caprae L.
       O. cernua Thunb.
 11 *O. incarnata L.

BALSAMINACEAE
171 IMPATIENS L.

   1 I. noli-tangere L.
   2 *I. capensis Meerb.
       I. biflora Walt.; *I. fulva* Nutt.
   3 *I. parviflora DC.
   4 *I. glandulifera Royle

*SIMAROUBACEAE
172 *AILANTHUS Desf.

   1 *A. altissima (Mill.) Swingle

ACERACEAE
173 ACER L.

   1 *A. pseudoplatanus L.
   2 *A. platanoides L.
   3 A. campestre L.

*STAPHYLEACEAE
174 *STAPHYLEA L.

   1 *S. pinnata L.

*HIPPOCASTANACEAE

175 *AESCULUS L.
    1 *A. hippocastanum L.

AQUIFOLIACEAE

176 ILEX L.
    1 I. aquifolium L.

CELASTRACEAE

177 EUONYMUS L.
    1 E. europaeus L.

BUXACEAE

178 BUXUS L.
    1 B. sempervirens L.

RHAMNACEAE

179 RHAMNUS L.
    1 R. catharticus L.
    2 *R. alaternus L.

180 FRANGULA Mill.
    1 F. alnus Mill.
      Rhamnus frangula L.

*VITACEAE

181 *VITIS L.
    1 *V. vinifera L.

182 *PARTHENOCISSUS Planch.
    1 *P. tricuspidata (Sieb. & Zucc.) Planch.
      Vitis thunbergii Druce, non Sieb. & Zucc.
    2 *P. quinquefolia (L.) Planch.
      Vitis hederacea Ehrh.

LEGUMINOSAE

183 *LUPINUS L.
    1 *L. nootkatensis Donn ex Sims
    2 *L. arboreus Sims

184 *LABURNUM Medic.
    1 *L. anagyroides Medic.
       L. laburnum (L.) Dörfl.

185 GENISTA L.
    1 G. tinctoria L.
    2 G. anglica L.
    3 G. pilosa L.

186 *SPARTIUM L.
    1 *S. junceum L.

187 ULEX L.
    1 U. europaeus L.
    2 U. gallii Planch.
    3 U. minor Roth
       U. nanus T. F. Forst.

188 SAROTHAMNUS Wimm.
    1 S. scoparius (L.) Wimm. ex Koch
       Cytisus scoparius (L.) Link
    a   subsp. scoparius
    b   subsp. maritimus (Rouy) Ulbr.
       S. scoparius subsp. *prostratus* (C. Bail.) Tutin

189 ONONIS L.
    1 O. repens L.
       O. repens × spinosa
    2 O. spinosa L.
    3 O. reclinata L.

190 MEDICAGO L.
    1 M. falcata L.
       M. falcata × sativa = M. × varia Martyn
       M. silvestris Fr.
    2 *M. sativa L.
    3 M. lupulina L.
    4 M. minima (L.) Bartal.
    5 M. polymorpha L.
       M. hispida Gaertn.; *M. lappacea* Desr.; *M. apiculata*
         Willd.; *M. denticulata* Willd.
    6 M. arabica (L.) Huds.
       M. maculata Sibth.

191 *MELILOTUS Mill.

1 *M. altissima Thuill.
   M. officinalis auct.
2 *M. officinalis (L.) Pall.
   M. petitpierreana Willd.; *M. arvensis* Wallr.
3 *M. alba Medic.
4 *M. indica (L.) All.

192 TRIFOLIUM L.
   Falcatula Brot.

1 T. ornithopodioides L.
   Trigonella purpurascens Lam.; *T. ornithopodioides*
      (L.) DC.; *Falcatula ornithopodioides* (L.) Brot.
      ex Bab.
2 T. pratense L.
3 T. ochroleucon Huds.
4 T. medium L.
5 T. squamosum L.
   T. maritimum Huds.
6 *T. stellatum L.
7 *T. incarnatum L.
8 T. molinerii Balb. ex Hornem.
9 T. arvense L.
10 T. striatum L.
11 T. scabrum L.
12 T. bocconei Savi
13 T. subterraneum L.
14 T. strictum L.
15 T. glomeratum L.
16 T. suffocatum L.
17 *T. hybridum L.
   T. elegans Savi
18 T. repens L.
19 T. fragiferum L.
20 *T. resupinatum L.
21 T. campestre Schreb.
   T. procumbens auct.
22 *T. aureum Poll.
   T. agrarium auct.
23 T. dubium Sibth.
24 T. micranthum Viv.
   T. filiforme L., *nom. ambig.*

LEGUMINOSAE

193 ANTHYLLIS L.
> 1 A. vulneraria L.
> *A. rubra* Gouan; *A. maritima* Schweigg.

194 *DORYCNIUM Mill.
> 1 *D. gracile Jord.
> *D. suffruticosum* auct.

195 LOTUS L.
> 1 L. corniculatus L.
> 2 L. tenuis Waldst. & Kit. ex Willd.
> 3 L. uliginosus Schkuhr
> *L. major* auct.
> 4 L. hispidus Desf. ex DC.
> 5 L. angustissimus L.
> *L. davyae* Druce

196 *TETRAGONOLOBUS Scop.
> 1 *T. maritimus (L.) Roth
> *Lotus siliquosus* L.; *Tetragonolobus siliquosus* Roth

197 *GALEGA L.
> 1 *G. officinalis L.

198 *ROBINIA L.
> 1 *R. pseudoacacia L.

199 *COLUTEA L.
> 1 *C. arborescens L.

200 ASTRAGALUS L.
> 1 A. danicus Retz.
> 2 A. alpinus L.
> 3 A. glycyphyllos L.
> 4 *A. boeticus L.
> 5 *A. odoratus Lam.

201 OXYTROPIS DC.
> 1 O. halleri Bunge
> *O. sericea* (DC.) Simonk., non Nutt.; *O. uralensis* auct.
> 2 O. campestris (L.) DC.

39

LEGUMINOSAE

202 ORNITHOPUS L.
Artrolobium Desv.
1 O. perpusillus L.
2 O. pinnatus (Mill.) Druce
O. ebracteatus Brot.; *Artrolobium pinnatum* (Mill.) Britten & Rendle

203 *CORONILLA L.
1 *C. varia L.
2 *C. glauca L.

204 HIPPOCREPIS L.
1 H. comosa L.

205 ONOBRYCHIS Mill.
1 O. viciifolia Scop.
O. sativa Lam.; *O. onobrychis* (L.) Karst.

206 VICIA L.
1 V. hirsuta (L.) Gray
2 V. tetrasperma (L.) Schreb.
3 V. tenuissima (Bieb.) Schinz & Thell.
V. gracilis Lois., non Soland.; *V. varia* (Brot.) Lacaita, non Host
4 V. cracca L.
5 *V. tenuifolia Roth
6 *V. villosa Roth
7 *V. dasycarpa Ten.
8 *V. cassubica L.
9 V. orobus DC.
10 V. sylvatica L.
11 V. sepium L.
12 V. lutea L.
V. laevigata Sm.
13†*V. hybrida L.
14 *V. sativa L.
15 V. angustifolia L.
V. bobartii E. Forst.
16 V. lathyroides L.
17 V. bithynica (L.) L.
18 *V. narbonensis L.

40

207 LATHYRUS L.
    1 L. aphaca L.
    2 L. nissolia L.
    3 *L. hirsutus L.
    4 L. pratensis L.
    5 *L. tuberosus L.
    6 L. sylvestris L.
    7 *L. heterophyllus L.
    8 *L. latifolius L.
    9 L. palustris L.
  10 L. japonicus Willd.
         L. maritimus Bigel.
  11 L. montanus Bernh.
         L. macrorrhizus Wimm.
  12 *L. niger (L.) Bernh.

ROSACEAE

208 *PHYSOCARPUS (Cambess.) Maxim.
    1 *P. opulifolius (L.) Maxim.
         Spiraea opulifolia L.

209 *SPIRAEA L.
    1 *S. salicifolia L.
    2 *S. douglasii Hook.

210 FILIPENDULA Mill.
    1 F. vulgaris Moench
         Spiraea filipendula L.; *Filipendula hexapetala* Gilib.
    2 F. ulmaria (L.) Maxim.
         Spiraea ulmaria L.

211 RUBUS L.
    1 R. chamaemorus L.
    2 R. saxatilis L.
    3 †R. arcticus L.
    4 *R. odoratus L.
    5 *R. parviflorus Nutt.
         R. nutkanus Moç. ex Ser.
    6 R. idaeus L.
    7 *R. phoenicolasius Maxim.
    8 *R. spectabilis Pursh

ROSACEAE

9 R. caesius L.
  R. caesius × idaeus
  R. caesius × fruticosus
10 *R. loganobaccus L. H. Bail.
11 R. fruticosus L. *sensu lato*[1]

(Sect. Suberecti P. J. Muell.)

  1 R. nessensis W. Hall
     R. suberectus Anders. ex. Sm.
  2 R. scissus W. C. R. Wats.
     R. fissus auct.
  3 R. sulcatus Vest ex Tratt.
  4 R. opacus Focke ex Bertram
     R. bertramii G. Braun ex Focke
  5 R. plicatus Weihe & Nees
  6 R. ammobius Focke
  7 R. fissus Lindl.
     R. rogersii E. F. Linton
  8 R. arrheniiformis W. C. R. Wats.
  9 R. affinis Weihe & Nees
  10 R. holerythros Focke ex Rogers
     R. briggsianus (Rogers) Sudre; *R. subopacus* auct.
  11 R. nobilissimus (W. C. R. Wats.) Pearsall
     R. nitidus subsp. *opacus* Rogers *pro parte*; *R. opacus* auct.
  12 R. divaricatus P. J. Muell.
     R. nitidus Weihe & Nees, non Raf.
  13 R. integribasis P. J. Muell.

(Sect. Triviales P. J. Muell.)

  14 R. conjungens (Bab.) W. C. R. Wats.
     R. corylifolius var. *conjungens* Bab.; *R. corylifolius* var. *cyclophyllus* Rogers *pro parte*
  15 R. ooliticus W. C. R. Wats.
  16 R. eboracensis W. C. R. Wats.
  17 R. sublustris Lees
     R. corylifolius var. *sublustris* (Lees) Rogers
  18 R. latifolius Bab.
  19 R. bucknallii J. W. White
  20 R. umbelliformis Muell. & Lefèv.
  21 R. balfourianus Bloxam ex Bab.

---

[1] The arrangement of the microspecies under this aggregate is based, by permission, on that of the late W. C. R. Watson, whose work is just published. For convenience sectional headings are inserted in parentheses, but it must be understood that these "sections" or groupings do not correspond to sections as generally interpreted in other genera.

22 R. warrenii Sudre
    R. dumetorum var. *concinnus* Bak. ex Warren
23 R. adenoleucus Chaboiss.
24 R. wahlbergii Arrhen.
25 R. halsteadensis W. C. R. Wats.
    R. dumetorum var. *raduliformis* A. Ley; *R. raduli-*
    formis (A. Ley) W. C. R. Wats., non Sudre
26 R. purpureicaulis W. C. R. Wats.
27 R. tuberculatus Bab.
    R. dumetorum var. *tuberculatus* (Bab.) Rogers
28 R. babingtonianus W. C. R. Wats.
    R. dumetorum var. *fasciculatus* Rogers *pro parte*;
    R. altheaefolius auct.
29 R. rubriflorus Purchas
    R. dumetorum var. *rubriflorus* (Purchas) Rogers
30 R. scabrosus P. J. Muell.
    R. dumetorum var. *ferox* auct.
31 R. myriacanthus Focke
    R. dumetorum var. *diversifolius* Rogers *pro parte*;
    R. dumetorum var. *pilosus* auct.
32 R. britannicus Rogers
    R. dumetorum var. *britannicus* (Rogers) Rogers
33 R. tenuiarmatus Lees
    R. dumetorum var. *triangularis* A. Ley

(Sect. Sylvatici P. J. Muell.)

34 R. gratus Focke
35 R. confertiflorus W. C. R. Wats.
    R. holerythros auct.
36 R. monensis Barton & Riddelsd.
37 R. vulgaris Weihe & Nees
38 R. latiarcuatus W. C. R. Wats.
39 R. subintegribasis Druce
    R. caeresiensis var. *integribasis* Riddelsd.; *R.*
    integribasis auct.
40 R. averyanus W. C. R. Wats.
41 R. dasycoccus W. C. R. Wats.
42 R. calvatus Lees ex Bloxam
43 R. sciocharis Sudre
44 R. nitidoides W. C. R. Wats.
45 R. ludensis W. C. R. Wats.
    R. sciaphilus auct.
46 R. crespignyanus W. C. R. Wats.
    R. similatus auct.
47 R. carpinifolius Weihe & Nees
48 R. chloophyllus Sudre

49 R. polyoplus W. C. R. Wats.
    R. perarmatus W. C. R. Wats., non Boulay ex
    Malbranche; *R. euoplus* W. C. R. Wats., non
    Foerst.; *R. salteri* auct.
50 R. horridisepalus Sudre
51 R. glanduliger W. C. R. Wats.
52 R. nemoralis P. J. Muell.
    R. selmeri Lindeb.; *R. pistoris* Barton & Riddelsd.
53 R. questieri Muell. & Lefèv.
54 *R. laciniatus Willd.
55 R. oxyanchus Sudre
    R. nemoralis auct.
56 R. cambrensis W. C. R. Wats.
57 R. durescens W. R. Linton
58 R. pullifolius W. C. R. Wats.
59 R. lindleianus Lees
60 R. egregius Focke
    R. mercicus var. *bracteatus* Bagnall
    R. egregius × ulmifolius
61 R. leucandrus Focke
62 R. mercicus Bagnall
63 · R. maassii Focke ex Bertram
64 R. muenteri Marss.
65 R. sampaianus Sudre
66 R. macrophyllus Weihe & Nees
67 R. subinermoides Druce
    R. subinermoides × ulmifolius
68 R. schlechtendalii Weihe ex Link
69 R. boulayi (Sudre) W. C. R. Wats.
70 R. sylvicola Muell. & Lefèv.
71 R. megaphyllus P. J. Muell.
72 R. majusculus Sudre
73 R. bakeranus Barton & Riddelsd.
74 R. silvaticus Weihe & Nees
75 R. chrysoxylon (Rogers) Sudre
76 R. patuliformis Sudre
77 R. amplificatus Lees
78 R. eglandulosus Muell. & Lefèv.
79 R. belophorus Muell. & Lefèv.
80 R. pyramidalis Kalt.
81 R. albionis W. C. R. Wats.
    R. macrophyllus subsp. *schlechtendalii* Rogers *pro
    parte*; *R. schlechtendalii* var. *anglicus* Sudre
82 R. mollissimus Rogers
83 R. crudelis W. C. R. Wats.
    R. colemanni auct.
84 R. amphichloros P. J. Muell.

ROSACEAE

85   R. hirtifolius Muell. & Wirtg.
86   R. orbifolius Lefèv.
87   R. obesifolius W. C. R. Wats.
        R. grabowskii auct.
88   R. macrophylloides Genev.
89   R. danicus (Focke) Focke
        R. purbeckensis Barton & Riddelsd.
90   R. londinensis (Rogers) W. C. R. Wats.
        R. daveyi Rilstone
91   R. libertianus Weihe ex Lejeune & Court.
92   R. ramosus Bloxam ex Briggs
93   R. salteri Bab.
94   R. pedatifolius Genev.
95   R. poliodes W. C. R. Wats.
96   R. rhodanthus W. C. R. Wats.
        R. rhombifolius auct.
97   R. insularis Aresch.
98   R. broensis W. C. R. Wats.
99   R. septentrionalis W. C. R. Wats.
100   R. stanneus Barton & Riddelsd.
101   R. atrocaulis P. J. Muell.
102   R. macroacanthos Weihe & Nees
103   R. incurvatus Bab.
104   R. villicaulis Koehl. ex Weihe & Nees
        R. castrensis W.-Dod
105   R. iricus Rogers
106   R. langei Jensen ex Frider. & Gelert
107   R. favonii W. C. R. Wats.
        R. buttii Barton & Riddelsd.
108   R. riddelsdellii Rilstone
109   R. lasiothyrsus Sudre
110   R. consobrinus Sudre
111   R. cariensis Rip. & Genev.
112   R. incarnatus P. J. Muell.
113   R. polyanthemus Lindeb.
        R. pulcherrimus Neum., non Hook.
114   R. rubritinctus W. C. R. Wats.
        R. cryptadenes Sudre, non Dumort.
115   R. rhombifolius Weihe ex Boenn.
        R. argenteus Weihe & Nees, non C. C. Gmel.
116   R. acclivitatum W. C. R. Wats.
        R. clivicola (A. Ley) Druce, non Sudre
117   R. prolongatus Boulay & Letendre
        R. griseoviridis Barton & Riddelsd.
118   R. alterniflorus Muell. & Lefèv.
119   R. herefordensis Sudre
        R. pubescens auct.

45

120 R. obvallatus Boulay & Gillot
121 R. separinus Genev.
  R. *cissburiensis* Barton & Riddelsd.; R. *gelertii* auct.
122 R. septicola Sudre
123 R. cardiophyllus Muell. & Lefèv.
  R. *furnarius* Barton & Riddelsd.; R. *rhamnifolius* auct.
124 R. rotundatus P. J. Muell. ex Genev.
  R. *dumnoniensis* Bab.; R. *altiarcuatus* Barton & Riddelsd.; R. *cariensis* auct.
125 R. lindebergii P. J. Muell.
  R. *lacustris* Rogers
126 R. errabundus W. C. R. Wats.
  R. *scheutzii* auct.
127 R. imbricatus Hort
128 R. silurum (A. Ley) W. C. R. Wats.

(Sect. Discolores P. J. Muell.)
129 R. ulmifolius Schott
  R. *rusticanus* Merc.; R. *discolor* auct.
  R. ulmifolius × villicaulis
  R. ulmifolius × vestitus
130 R. pseudobifrons Sudre
  R. pseudobifrons × ulmifolius
131 R. chloocladus W. C. R. Wats.
  R. *pubescens* Weihe ex Boenn., non Raf.
132 R. winteri P. J. Muell. ex Focke
133 R. crassifolius Genev.
  R. *propinquus* P. J. Muell., non Richardson; R. *lamburnensis* Rilstone; R. *argentatus* auct.
  R. crassifolius × londinensis = R. × carnkiefensis Rilstone
  R. crassifolius × stanneus
  R. crassifolius × rubritinctus
  R. crassifolius × prolongatus = R. × pydarensis Rilstone
  R. crassifolius × rufescens
134 R. stenopetalus Muell. & Lefèv.
135 R. geniculatus Kalt.
136 R. cuspidifer Muell. & Lefèv.
137 R. bifrons Vest ex Tratt.
  R. *cornubiensis* (Rogers & Riddelsd.) Rilstone
  R. bifrons × londinensis = R. × tresidderi Rilstone
138 R. vulnificus Lefèv. ex Genev.
139 *R. procerus P. J. Muell.
  R. *oplothyrsus* Sudre

46

140 R. neomalacus Sudre
141 R. falcatus Kalt.
  R. thyrsoideus auct.
142 R. hylophilus Rip. ex Genev.
  R. brittonii Barton & Riddelsd.
143 R. thyrsanthus Focke

(Sect. Sprengeliani (Focke) W. C. R. Wats.)

144 R. braeuckeri G. Braun
  R. hemistemon auct.
145 R. chlorothyrsos Focke
146 R. sprengelii Weihe
147 R. lentiginosus Lees
148 R. permundus W. C. R. Wats.
149 R. arrhenii (Lange) Lange
150 R. axillaris Lejeune

(Sect. Appendiculati (Genev.) Sudre)

151 R. nemorensis Muell. & Lefèv.
152 R. hesperius Rogers
  R. myricae var. *hesperius* (Rogers) Rogers
153 R. fuscicortex Sudre
  R. podophyllos auct.
154 R. silesiacus Weihe
155 R. eriostachys Muell. & Lefèv.
156 R. helveticus Gremli
157 R. lasiostachys Muell. & Lefèv.
  R. surrejanus Barton & Riddelsd.; *R. hirtior* W. C. R. Wats.; *R. leucanthemus* auct.
158 R. cinerosiformis Rilstone
159 R. serratulifolius Sudre
160 R. hebecaulis Sudre
  R. thurstonii Rilstone
161 R. orbus W. C. R. Wats.
162 R. schmidelyanus Sudre
163 R. flavescens Muell. & Lefèv.
164 R. condensatus P. J. Muell.
165 R. vestitus Weihe & Nees
  R. diversifolius Lindl.; *R. leucostachys* auct.
166 R. podophyllos P. J. Muell.
167 R. conspicuus P. J. Muell.
168 R. andegavensis Bouvet
  R. umbrosus auct.
169 R. salisburgensis Focke
170 R. adscitus Genev.
  R. hypoleucus Muell. & Lefèv, non Vest

171 R. leucostachys Schleich. ex Sm.
    R. lasioclados auct.
172 R. scutulifolius Sudre
173 R. boraeanus Genev.
174 R. conspersus W. C. R. Wats.
175 R. magnificus P. J. Muell. ex Genev.
176 R. acutidens Boulay & Gillot
177 R. macrothyrsus Lange
178 R. criniger (E. F. Linton) Rogers
179 R. eifeliensis Wirtg.
180 R. melanocladus Sudre
181 R. mucronatiformis Sudre
182 R. mucronulatus Bor.
    R. mucronatus Bloxam, non Ser.; *R. mucronifer*
    Sudre
183 R. drejeri Jensen
184 R. badius Focke
185 R. mulleri Lefèv.
186 R. briggsii Bloxam
187 R. cinerosus Rogers
188 R. atrichantherus E. H. L. Krause
189 R. lettii Rogers
190 R. gelertii Frider.
191 R. leyanus Rogers
192 R. hibernicus (Rogers) W. C. R. Wats.
    R. drejeri var. *hibernicus* Rogers
193 R. dunensis Rogers
194 R. hypomalacus Focke
    R. mucronatoides A. Ley
195 R. chaerophyllus Sag. & Schultze
196 R. bracteosus Weihe ex Lejeune & Court.
    R. orthoclados A. Ley, non Boulay
197 R. dentatifolius (Briggs) W. C. R. Wats.
198 R. ahenifolius W. C. R. Wats.
199 R. daltrii Edees & Rilstone
200 R. gremlii Focke
201 R. taeniarum Lindeb.
    R. spurius Neum., non Hal. & Braun; *R. infestus*
    auct.
202 R. iodnephes W. C. R. Wats.
203 R. mercieri Genev.
204 R. radula Weihe ex Boenn.
    R. radula × ulmifolius = R. × cotteswoldensis Barton
    & Riddelsd.
205 †R. pustulatus P. J. Muell. ex Sudre
206 R. sectiramus W. C. R. Wats.
207 R. macrostachys P. J. Muell.

208 R. adenanthus Boulay & Gillot
209 R. genevieri Bor.
210 R. crispus Muell. & Lefèv.
 R. crispus × vestitus
211 R. uncinatiformis Sudre
212 R. discerptus P. J. Muell.
 R. echinatus auct.
213 R. echinatoides (Rogers) Sudre
 R. radula var. *echinatoides* Rogers
214 R. aspericaulis Muell. & Lefèv.
215 R. malacotrichus Sudre
216 R. rudis Weihe & Nees
217 R. radulicaulis Sudre
 R. ericetorum var. *sertiflorus* Rogers *pro parte*
218 R. prionodontus Muell. & Lefèv.
219 R. granulatus Muell. & Lefèv.
220 R. regillus A. Ley
221 R. micans Gren. & Godr.
 R. wolley-dodii Sudre
222 R. pulcher Muell. & Lefèv.
223 R. foliosus Weihe & Nees
 R. flexuosus Muell. & Lefèv.; *R. saltuum* Focke;
 R. hyposericeus Sudre
224 R. rubristylus W. C. R. Wats.
 R. newbouldii Druce, non Bab.
225 R. pseudadenanthus W. C. R. Wats.
 R. adenanthus auct.
226 R. subtercanens W. C. R. Wats.
227 R. sagittarius Riddelsd.
 R. mutabilis subsp. *nemorosus* Rogers *pro parte*
228 R. teretiusculus Kalt.
229 R. bloxamii Lees
230 R. largificus W. C. R. Wats.
231 R. cavatifolius P. J. Muell.
232 R. corymbosus P. J. Muell.
233 R. exsolutus Muell. & Lefèv.
234 R. fuscus Weihe & Nees
 R. fusciformis Sudre
235 R. acutipetalus Muell. & Lefèv.
236 R. trichodes W. C. R. Wats.
 R. hirtus subsp. *rubiginosus* Rogers *pro parte*; *R.*
 foliosus auct.
237 R. hirsutus Wirtg.
238 R. hirsutissimus Sudre & Ley
239 R. adamsii Sudre
 R. babingtonii var. *phyllothyrsus* Rogers *pro parte*
240 R. watsonii W. H. Mills

241   R. apiculatiformis Sudre
242   R. racemiger Gremli
243   R. pallidus Weihe & Nees
244   R. drymophilus Muell. & Lefèv.
245   R. loehrii Wirtg.
246   R. spadix W. C. R. Wats.
       R. podophyllos auct.
247   R. chlorocaulon Sudre
       R. coombensis Rilstone
248   R. menkei Weihe & Nees
       R. tereticaulis auct.
249   R. morganwgensis Barton & Riddelsd.
250   R. argutifolius Muell. & Lefèv.
       R. glareosus Rogers; *R. monachus* auct.
251   R. acutifrons A. Ley
252   R. euryanthemus W. C. R. Wats.
253   R. insectifolius Muell. & Lefèv.
       R. nuticeps Barton & Riddelsd.
254   R. brachyadenes P. J. Muell.
255   R. foliolatus Muell. & Lefèv.
256   R. aciphyllus Sudre
257   R. erubescens Wirtg.
258   R. microdontus Muell. & Lefèv.
259   R. thyrsiflorus Weihe & Nees
       R. hirtus subsp. *flaccidifolius* Rogers *pro parte*
260   R. derasifolius Sudre
261   R. putneiensis W. C. R. Wats.
       R. rhenanus auct.
262   R. curtiglandulosus Sudre
263   R. scaber Weihe & Nees
       R. scaber × ulmifolius
264   R. tereticaulis P. J. Muell.
265   R. praetextus Sudre
266   R. derasus Muell. & Lefèv.
267   R. vallisparsus Sudre
268   R. frondicomus Foerst.
269   R. longithyrsiger Lees ex Bak.
       R. pyramidalis (Bab.) Bab., non Kalt.
270   R. omalodontos Muell. & Wirtg.
271   R. truncifolius Muell. & Lefèv.
       R. peninsulae Rilstone
272   R. concolor W. Ley
273   R. cyclophorus Sudre
274   R. pseudobellardii (Sudre) W. C. R. Wats.
275   R. luteistylus Sudre
276   R. scaberrimus Sudre
277   R. laxatifrons W. C. R. Wats.

ROSACEAE

278 R. obcuneatus Muell. & Lefèv.
   R. cenomanensis Sudre; *R. botryeros* (Rogers) Rogers; *R. oigocladus* auct.
279 R. obscurissimus Sudre
280 R. entomodontos P. J. Muell.
   R. macranthelos auct.
281 R. erraticus Sudre
   R. fuscus subsp. *obscurus* Rogers *pro parte*
282 R. adornatiformis Sudre
283 R. obscurus Kalt.
284 R. rufescens Muell. & Lefèv.
285 R. purchasianus (Rogers) Rogers
   R. rosaceus var. *purchasianus* Rogers
286 R. cruentatus P. J. Muell.
287 R. grypoacanthus Muell. & Lefèv.
288 R. aggregatus Kalt.
289 R. fuscoviridis Rilstone
290 R. sprengeliiflorus Sudre
291 R. obscuriformis Sudre
292 R. insericatus P. J. Muell. ex Wirtg.
   R. newbouldianus Rilstone
293 R. rhombophyllus Muell. & Lefèv.
294 R. gravetii Boulay ex Sudre
295 R. apiculatus Weihe & Nees
   R. anglosaxonicus Gelert; *R. curvidens* A. Ley
296 R. heterobelus Sudre
   R. penhallowensis Rilstone; *R. praeruptorum* auct.
297 R. raduloides (Rogers) Sudre
298 R. melanoxylon Muell. & Wirtg.
299 R. pascuorum W. C. R. Wats.
300 R. longifrons W. C. R. Wats.
   R. longifrons × ulmifolius
301 R. melanodermis Focke
302 R. inopacatus Muell. & Lefèv.
303 R. reichenbachii Koehl. ex Weihe & Nees
304 R. retrodentatus Muell. & Lefèv.
   R. vectensis W. C. R. Wats.; *R. borreri* auct.
305 R. phaeocarpus W. C. R. Wats.
   R. babingtonii auct.
306 R. griffithianus Rogers
307 R. indusiatus Focke
308 R. euanthinus W. C. R. Wats.
   R. apiculatus var. *vestitiformis* (Rogers) Riddelsd.
309 R. tardus W. C. R. Wats.
310 R. leightonii Lees ex Leighton
   R. radula var. *anglicanus* Rogers

51

ROSACEAE

311 R. disjunctus Muell. & Lefèv.
     R. cuneatus (Rogers & Ley) Druce, non Boulay;
     R. moylei Barton & Riddelsd.; *R. ericetorum*
     auct.
312 R. diversus W. C. R. Wats.
     R. hirtus subsp. *kaltenbachii* Rogers *pro parte*
313 R. hostilis Muell. & Wirtg.
     R. hostilis × ulmifolius
314 R. wedgwoodiae Barton & Riddelsd.
315 R. furvicolor Focke
     R. melanoxylon auct.
316 R. angusticuspis Sudre
     R. apiculatus var. *setulosus* (Rogers) Riddelsd.
317 R. squalidus Genev.
     R. naldretti (J. W. White) W. C. R. Wats.
318 R. pseudoplinthostylus W. C. R. Wats.
     R. plinthostylus auct.
319 R. mutabilis Genev.
320 R. turneri W. C. R. Wats.
     R. glandulosus auct.
321 R. powellii Rogers
     R. histrix var. *powellii* (Rogers) Riddelsd.
322 R. rotundifolius (Bab.) Bloxam
     R. hiernii Riddelsd.
323 R. rosaceus Weihe & Nees
324 R. formidabilis Muell. & Lefèv.
325 R. hastiformis W. C. R. Wats.
     R. thyrsiger Bab., non Banning & Focke
326 R. lejeunei Weihe & Nees
327 R. festivus Muell. & Wirtg.
328 R. breconensis W. C. R. Wats.
     R. lejeunei auct.
329 R. rilstonei Barton & Riddelsd.

(Sect. Glandulosi P. J. Muell.)
330 R. murrayi Sudre
     R. histrix var. *adornatus* auct.
331 R. pygmaeopsis Focke
332 R. newbridgensis Barton & Riddelsd.
333 R. ochrodermis A. Ley
334 R. coronatus Boulay
335 R. adornatus P. J. Muell. ex Wirtg.
336 R. saxicola P. J. Muell.
337 R. chenonii Sudre
338 R. pilocarpus Gremli
339 R. abietinus Sudre
340 R. bavaricus (Focke) Sudre

341   R. mikanii Koehl. ex Weihe
342   R. spinulifer Muell. & Lefèv.
  R. tumulorum Rilstone; *R. koehleri* auct.
  R. spinulifer × ulmifolius
343   R. horridicaulis P. J. Muell.
344   R. apricus Wimm.
345   R. humifusus Weihe & Nees
346   R. plinthostylus Genev.
347   R. rotundellus Sudre
348   R. hylocharis W. C. R. Wats.
349   R. scabripes Genev.
  R. rosaceus auct.
350   R. koehleri Weihe & Nees
  R. vigursii Rilstone
351   R. aculeatissimus Kalt.
  R. rosaceus auct.
352   R. histrix Weihe & Nees
353   R. semiglaber (Rogers) W. C. R. Wats.
354   R. infestus Weihe ex Boenn.
  R. setulosus Muell. & Lefèv.
355   R. adenolobus W. C. R. Wats.
356   R. dasyphyllus (Rogers) Rogers
  R. koehleri subsp. *dasyphyllus* (Rogers) Rogers
357   R. marshallii Focke & Rogers
358   R. billotii P. J. Muell.
359   R. hartmanii Gandog. ex Sudre
360   R. lapeyrousianus Sudre
361   R. asperidens Sudre
362   R. emarginatus P. J. Muell.
363   R. fuscoater Weihe & Nees
364   R. absconditus Muell. & Lefèv.
365   R. oigocladus Muell. & Lefèv.
366   R. aristisepalus (Sudre) W. C. R. Wats.
  R. inaequabilis var. *aristisepalus* Sudre; *R. vela-*
  tus auct.
367   R. hypochlorus Sudre
368   R. hebecarpos P. J. Muell.
369   R. spinulatus Boulay
370   R. schleicheri Weihe ex Tratt.
371   R. viridis Kalt.
372   R. dissectifolius Sudre
373   R. graciliflorens Sudre
374   R. hirtus Waldst. & Kit.
375   R. bellardii Weihe & Nees
376   R. pallidisetus Sudre
  R. angustifrons var. *pallidisetus* (Sudre) Sudre;
  R. divexiramus auct.

377 R. guentheri Weihe & Nees
378 R. perplexus P. J. Muell.
379 R. rubiginosus P. J. Muell.
380 R. nigricatus Muell. & Lefèv.
381 R. purpuratus Sudre
382 R. durotrigum R. P. Murr.
383 R. leptadenes Sudre
384 R. lintonii Focke ex Bab.
385 R. elegans P. J. Muell.
    R. angustifrons Sudre; *R. serpens* auct.
386 R. incultus Wirtg.
387 R. hylonomus Muell. & Lefèv.
388 R. analogus Muell. & Lefèv.
389 R. lusaticus Rostock

212 POTENTILLA L.
    Comarum L.

1 P. fruticosa L.
2 P. palustris (L.) Scop.
    Comarum palustre L.; *Potentilla comarum* Nestl.
3 P. sterilis (L.) Garcke
    P. fragariastrum Pers.
4 P. rupestris L.
5 P. anserina L.
6 P. argentea L.
7 *P. recta L.
8 *P. norvegica L.
9 *P. intermedia L.
10 *P. thuringiaca Bernh. ex Link
    P. parviflora Gaudin, non Desf.
11 P. tabernaemontani Aschers.
    P. verna auct.
12 P. crantzii (Crantz) G. Beck ex Fritsch
    P. cryeri Druce; *P. salisburgensis* auct.
13 P. erecta (L.) Räusch.
    P. silvestris Neck.; *P. tormentilla* Stokes
    P. erecta × reptans = P. × italica Lehm.
14 P. anglica Laichard.
    P. procumbens Sibth.
    P. anglica × erecta = P. × suberecta Zimmet.
    P. anglica × reptans = P. × mixta Nolte ex Reichb.
15 P. reptans L.

ROSACEAE

213 SIBBALDIA L.
  1 S. procumbens L.
     Potentilla sibbaldi Haller f.

214 *DUCHESNEA Sm.
  1 *D. indica (Andr.) Focke
     Fragaria indica Andr.

215 FRAGARIA L.
  1 F. vesca L.
  2 *F. moschata Duchesne
     F. elatior Ehrh.
  3 *F. ananassa Duchesne
     F. chiloensis auct.

216 GEUM L.
  1 G. urbanum L.
  2 *G. macrophyllum Willd.
  3 G. rivale L.
     G. rivale×urbanum=G.×intermedium Ehrh.

217 DRYAS L.
  1 D. octopetala L.

218 AGRIMONIA L.
  1 A. eupatoria L.
  2 A. odorata (Gouan) Mill.

219 *AREMONIA DC.
  1 *A. agrimonoides (L.) DC.
     Agrimonia agrimonoides L.

220 ALCHEMILLA L.
  1 A. alpina L.
  2 A. conjuncta Bab.
     A. argentea (Trevelyan) D. Don, non Lam.
  3 A. vulgaris L. *sensu lato*
    1 A. minor Huds.
      A. pubescens Lam.; *A. anglica* Rothm.
    2 A. vestita (Buser) Raunk.
      A. pseudominor Wilmott; *A. colorata* auct.; *A. subcrenata* auct.; *A. minor* auct.
    3 A. filicaulis Buser
      A. salmoniana Jaquet; *A. heteropoda* auct.; *A. tenuis* auct.

   4 A. subcrenata Buser
   5 A. minima Walters
   6 A. monticola Opiz
       A. pastoralis Buser; *A. crinita* auct.
   7 A. acutiloba Opiz
   8 A. xanthochlora Rothm.
       A. curtiloba auct.; *A. pratensis* auct.
   9 A. glomerulans Buser
       A. reniformis auct.
 10 A. glabra Neygenf.
       A. acuminatidens auct.; *A. alpestris* auct.;
       A. coriacea auct.; *A. obtusa* auct.
 11 A. wichurae (Buser) Stéfanss.
       A. acutidens auct.; *A. connivens* auct.; *A. firma* auct.
 12 *A. mollis (Buser) Rothm.

221 **APHANES L.**
   1 A. arvensis L.
      Alchemilla arvensis (L.) Scop.
   2 A. microcarpa (Boiss. & Reut.) Rothm.

222 **SANGUISORBA L.**
   1 S. officinalis L.
      Poterium officinale (L.) A. Gray
   2 *S. canadensis L.
      Poterium canadense (L.) A. Gray

223 **POTERIUM L.**
   1 P. sanguisorba L.
   2 *P. polygamum Waldst. & Kit.
      P. muricatum Spach

224 ***ACAENA Mutis ex L.**
   1 *A. anserinifolia (J. R. & G. Forst.) Druce

225 **ROSA L.**
   1 R. arvensis Huds.
      R. gallicoides (Bak.) Déségl.
      R. arvensis × stylosa=R. × bibracteoides W.-Dod
      R. arvensis × canina=R. × wheldonii W.-Dod
      R. arvina W.-Dod, non Krock.; *R. debilis* W.-Dod
      R. arvensis × obtusifolia=R. × concinnoides W.-Dod
      R. surreyana W.-Dod; ? *R. bickertonensis* W.-Dod
      R. arvensis × micrantha=R. × inelegans W.-Dod
      R. toddii W.-Dod

ROSACEAE

2 *R. sempervirens L.
3 *R. multiflora Thunb.
4 R. pimpinellifolia L.
    R. rubella Sm.; *R. spinosissima* auct.
    R. pimpinellifolia × tomentosa = R. × involuta Sm.
        R. wilsoni Borrer; *R. margerisoni* (W.-Dod) W.-Dod;
        R. pilosa (Lindl.) W.-Dod, non Opiz
    R. pimpinellifolia × sherardii = R. × gracilis Woods
        R. borealis W.-Dod, non Tratt.; *R. laevigata*
        (Bak.) W.-Dod, non Michx.; *R. robertsoni* (Bak.)
        W.-Dod
    R. pimpinellifolia × villosa = R. × sabinii Woods
        R. doniana Woods; *R. scotica* W.-Dod, non Mill.;
        R. mayoensis W.-Dod; *R. marshalli* W.-Dod
    R. pimpinellifolia × rubiginosa = R. × cantiana (W
    Dod) W.-Dod
        R. nicholsonii (Crép.) W.-Dod; *R. moorei* (Bak.)
        W.-Dod
    R. pimpinellifolia × rubiginosa × sherardii = R. × per-
    thensis Rouy
        R. barclayi W.-Dod
5 *R. rugosa Thunb.
6 *R. virginiana Mill.
7 R. stylosa Desv.
8 R. canina L.
    R. dumetorum Thuill.; *R. andegavensis* Bast.; *R.*
    lutetiana Léman; *R. urbica* Léman; *R. squarrosa*
    (Rau) Bor.; *R. deseglisei* Bor.; *R. blondaeana* Rip.
    ex Déségl.; *R. drucei* W.-Dod
    R. canina × pimpinellifolia = R. × hibernica Templeton
    R. canina × gallica (R. gallica L.) = R. × alba L.
    R. collina Jacq.
    R. canina × rugosa = R. × praegeri W.-Dod
    R. canina × stylosa = R. × rufescens W.-Dod
    R. canina × obtusifolia = R. × subobtusifolia W.-Dod
    R. canina × tomentosa = R. × curvispina W.-Dod
    ? *R. aberrans* W.-Dod
    R. canina × rubiginosa = R. × latens W.-Dod
    R. standeni W.-Dod
9 R. dumalis Bechst.
    R. glauca Vill. ex Lois., non Pourr.; *R. caesia* Sm.;
    R. coriifolia Fr.; *R. reuteri* (Godet) Reut.;
    R. afzeliana auct.

R. dumalis × pimpinellifolia=R. × setonensis W.-Dod
R. glabra (Bak.) W.-Dod, non Andr.
R. dumalis × tomentosa=R. × rogersii W.-Dod
10 R. obtusifolia Desv.
R. borreri Woods; *R. tomentella* Léman
R. obtusifolia × rubiginosa=R. × tomentelliformis W.-Dod
11 R. tomentosa Sm.
R. mollissima Willd., *nom. ambig.*
12 R. sherardii Davies
R. omissa Déségl.; *R. glaucoides* W.-Dod; *R. shool-bredii* W.-Dod
R. sherardii × tomentosa=R. × suberectiformis W.-Dod
13 R. villosa L.
R. pomifera Herrm.; *R. mollis* Sm.
14 R. rubiginosa L.
R. eglanteria auct.
R. rubiginosa × tomentosa=R. × burdonii W.-Dod
R. rubiginosa × sherardii
R. rubiginosa × villosa=R. × molliformis W.-Dod
15 R. micrantha Borrer ex Sm.
R. micrantha × rubiginosa
R. dubia W.-Dod, non Wibel
16 R. elliptica Tausch
17 R. agrestis Savi
R. agrestis × micrantha=R. × bishopii W.-Dod

226 PRUNUS L.

1 P. spinosa L.
P. communis auct.
2 *P. domestica L.
P. communis Huds.
a *subsp. domestica
b *subsp. insititia (L.) C. K. Schneid.
P. insititia L.
3 *P. cerasifera Ehrh.
4 P. avium (L.) L.
5 *P. cerasus L.
6 P. padus L.
7 *P. laurocerasus L.
8 *P. lusitanica L.

ROSACEAE

227 COTONEASTER Medic.
    1 C. integerrimus Medic.
        C. vulgaris Lindl.; *C. cotoneaster* (L.) Karst.
    2 *C. simonsii Bak.
    3 *C. horizontalis Decne.
    4 *C. microphyllus Wall. ex Lindl.
    5 *C. frigidus Wall. ex Lindl.

228 *PYRACANTHA M. J. Roem.
    1 *P. coccinea M. J. Roem.
        Crataegus pyracantha (L.) Medic.

229 CRATAEGUS L.
    1 C. oxyacanthoides Thuill.
        C. oxyacantha auct.
    2 C. monogyna Jacq.
        C. oxyacantha L., *nom. ambig.*
        C. monogyna × oxyacanthoides=C. × media Bechst.
    3 *C. orientalis Pall. ex Bieb.
    4 *C. punctata Jacq.
    5 *C. crus-galli L.

230 *MESPILUS L.
    1 *M. germanica L.
        Pyrus germanica (L.) Hook. f.

231 *AMELANCHIER Medic.
    1 *A. confusa Hyland.
        A. canadensis auct.; *A. laevis* auct.; *A. intermedia* auct.

232 SORBUS L.
    1 S. aucuparia L.
        Pyrus aucuparia (L.) Ehrh.
    2†*S. domestica L.
        Pyrus domestica (L.) Ehrh.
    3 S. pseudofennica E. F. Warb.
        Pyrus fennica Bab. *pro parte*; *Sorbus fennica* auct.
    4 S. intermedia (Ehrh.) Pers. *sensu lato*
        Pyrus intermedia Ehrh.
        1 *S. intermedia (Ehrh.) Pers.
            S. scandica (L.) Fr.; *Pyrus scandica* (L.) Bab.
        2 S. arranensis Hedl.
            Pyrus arranensis (Hedl.) Druce
        3 S. leyana Wilmott

4   S. minima (A. Ley) Hedl.
     Pyrus minima A. Ley
5   S. anglica Hedl.
     Pyrus anglica (Hedl.) Druce;   *Sorbus mougeoti*
     var. *anglica* (Hedl.) C. E. Salmon

5 S. aria (L.) Crantz *sensu lato*
  Pyrus aria (L.) Ehrh.

  1   S. aria (L.) Crantz
  2   S. leptophylla E. F. Warb.
  3   S. eminens E. F. Warb.
  4   S. hibernica E. F. Warb.
  5   S. porrigentiformis E. F. Warb.
     Pyrus porrigens Druce *pro parte*; *Sorbus porri-*
     gens auct.
  6   S. lancastriensis E. F. Warb.
  7   S. rupicola (Syme) Hedl.
     Pyrus rupicola (Syme) Bab.
  8   S. vexans E. F. Warb.

  S. aria × aucuparia=S. × thuringiaca (Ilse) Fritsch
  S. semipinnata Hedl., non Borbás
  S. aria × torminalis=S. × vagensis Wilmott
6 S. latifolia (Lam.) Pers. *sensu lato*
  Pyrus latifolia (Lam.) Syme
  1   S. bristoliensis Wilmott
  2   S. subcuneata Wilmott
  3   S. devoniensis E. F. Warb.

7 S. torminalis (L.) Crantz
  Pyrus torminalis (L.) Ehrh.

233 PYRUS L.
  1 *P. communis L.
  2 P. cordata Desv.

234 MALUS Mill.
  1 M. sylvestris Mill.
    Pyrus malus L.
  a   subsp. sylvestris
    M. pumila auct.
  b   *subsp. mitis (Wallr.) Mansf.

CRASSULACEAE
235 SEDUM L.
  1 S. rosea (L.) Scop.
    S. rhodiola DC.

2 S. telephium L.
   a subsp. purpurascens (Koch) Syme
      S. purpureum auct.
   b subsp. fabaria Syme
      S. fabaria Koch
3 *S. spurium Bieb.
      S. stoloniferum auct.
4 *S. dasyphyllum L.
5 S. anglicum Huds.
6 *S. album L.
   a subsp. album
   b subsp. micranthum (DC.) Syme
      S. micranthum Bast. ex DC.
7 *S. lydium Boiss.
8 S. acre L.
9 *S. sexangulare L.
10 S. forsteranum Sm.
   a subsp. forsteranum
   b subsp. elegans (Lejeune) E. F. Warb.
      S. rupestre auct.
11 *S. reflexum L.
      S. glaucum Haw., non Lam.
12 S. villosum L.
13 [*S. dendroideum Sessé & Moç. ex DC.]

236 *SEMPERVIVUM L.
  1 *S. tectorum L.

237 CRASSULA L.
   Tillaea L.
  1 C. tillaea L.-Garland
     Tillaea muscosa L.
  2 †C. aquatica (L.) Schönl.
     Tillaea aquatica L.

238 UMBILICUS DC.
  1 U. rupestris (Salisb.) Dandy
     U. pendulinus DC.; *Cotyledon umbilicus-veneris* auct.

SAXIFRAGACEAE
239 SAXIFRAGA L.
  1 S. nivalis L.
  2 S. stellaris L.
     S. crawfordii E. S. Marshall

3   S. hirculus L.
4   *S. umbrosa L.
5   S. spathularis Brot.
> S. *serratifolia* (D. Don) Mackay ex Reichb.; *S. umbrosa* auct.; *S. punctata* auct.

  *S. spathularis × umbrosa
> S. *umbrosa* var. *crenatoserrata* Bab.

6   S. hirsuta L.
> S. *geum* L. 1762, non L. 1753; *S. elegans* Mackay ex Reichb., non Zeyh. ex Schrank; *S. lactiflora* Pugsl.

> S. hirsuta × spathularis = S. × polita (Haw.) Link
> S. *hirsuta* auct.; *S. geum* auct.

7   *S. cymbalaria L.
8   S. tridactylites L.
9   S. granulata L.
10   S. cernua L.
11   S. rivularis L.
12   S. cespitosa L.
13   S. hartii D. A. Webb
14   S. rosacea Moench
> S. *decipiens* Ehrh. ex Pers.; *S. sternbergii* Willd.; *S. hirta* Donn ex Sm., non Haw.; *S. affinis* D. Don; *S. incurvifolia* D. Don; *S. drucei* E. S. Marshall; *S. groenlandica* auct.

15   S. hypnoides L.
> S. *viscosa* Haw.; *S. spatulata* Haw., non Desf.; *S. angustifolia* Haw.; *S. elongella* Sm., non Haw.; *S. platypetala* Sm.; *S. laetevirens* D. Don; *S. recurva* Bree ex Schleich.; *S. leptophylla* auct.; *S. sponhemica* auct.; *S. groenlandica* auct.

  S. hypnoides × rosacea
16   S. aizoides L.
17   S. oppositifolia L.

240 *TELLIMA R. Br.
  1 *T. grandiflora (Pursh) Dougl. ex Lindl.

241 *TOLMIEA Torr. & Gray
   Leptaxis Raf.
  1 *T. menziesii (Pursh) Torr. & Gray
> *Leptaxis menziesii* (Pursh) Raf.

242 CHRYSOSPLENIUM L.

   1 C. oppositifolium L.
   2 C. alternifolium L.

PARNASSIACEAE

243 PARNASSIA L.

   1 P. palustris L.

*HYDRANGEACEAE

244 *PHILADELPHUS L.

   1 *P. coronarius L.

*ESCALLONIACEAE

245 *ESCALLONIA Mutis ex L. f.

   1 *E. macrantha Hook. & Arn.

GROSSULARIACEAE

246 RIBES L.

   1 R. sylvestre (Lam.) Mert. & Koch
        R. rubrum auct.
   2 R. spicatum Robson
        R. pubescens (Hartm.) Hedl.; *R. petraeum* auct.
   3 R. nigrum L.
   4 *R. sanguineum Pursh
   5 R. alpinum L.
   6 R. uva-crispa L.
        R. grossularia L.

DROSERACEAE

247 DROSERA L.

   1 D. rotundifolia L.
   2 D. anglica Huds.
        D. anglica × rotundifolia = D. × obovata Mert. & Koch
   3 D. intermedia Hayne
        D. longifolia auct.

*SARRACENIACEAE

248 *SARRACENIA L.

   1 *S. purpurea L.

LYTHRACEAE

249 LYTHRUM L.

   1 L. salicaria L.
   2 L. hyssopifolia L.

250 PEPLIS L.

   1 P. portula L.

THYMELAEACEAE

251 DAPHNE L.

   1 D. mezereum L.
   2 D. laureola L.
      D. laureola × mezereum = D. × houtteana Lindl. & Paxt.

ELAEAGNACEAE

252 HIPPOPHAE L.

   1 H. rhamnoides L.

ONAGRACEAE

253 LUDWIGIA L.

   1 L. palustris (L.) Ell.

254 EPILOBIUM L.

   1 E. hirsutum L.
      E. hirsutum × parviflorum
        E. intermedium Ruhmer, non Mérat
      E. hirsutum × montanum = E. × erroneum Hausskn.
      E. hirsutum × lanceolatum = E. × surreyanum E. S. Marshall
      E. hirsutum × roseum = E. × goerzii Rubner
      E. hirsutum × lamyi
      E. hirsutum × obscurum = E. × anglicum E. S. Marshall
      E. hirsutum × palustre = E. × waterfallii E. S. Marshall
   2 E. parviflorum Schreb.
      E. parviflorum × roseum = E. × persicinum Reichb.
   3 E. montanum L.
      E. collinum auct.
      E. montanum × parviflorum = E. × limosum Schur

E. montanum × roseum = E. × mutabile Boiss. & Reut.
E. heterocaule Borbás

E. montanum × obscurum = E. × aggregatum Čelak.

E. montanum × palustre = E. × montaniforme Knaf ex Čelak.

4   E. lanceolatum Seb. & Mauri

E. lanceolatum × parviflorum = E. × aschersonianum Hausskn.

E. lanceolatum × montanum = E. × neogradense Borbás

E. lanceolatum × roseum = E. × abortivum Hausskn.

E. lanceolatum × obscurum = E. × lamotteanum Hausskn.

5   E. roseum Schreb.

6 *E. adenocaulon Hausskn.

E. adenocaulon × hirsutum

E. adenocaulon × parviflorum

E. adenocaulon × montanum

E. adenocaulon × lanceolatum

E. adenocaulon × roseum

E. adenocaulon × adnatum

E. adenocaulon × lamyi

E. adenocaulon × obscurum

E. adenocaulon × palustre

7   E. adnatum Griseb.

E. tetragonum auct.

E. adnatum × hirsutum = E. × brevipilum Hausskn.

E. adnatum × parviflorum = E. × weissenburgense F. W. Schultz

E. adnatum × montanum = E. × beckhausii Hausskn.

E. adnatum × roseum = E. × borbasianum Hausskn.

E. adnatum × lamyi = E. × semiadnatum Borbás

E. adnatum × obscurum = E. × thuringiacum Hausskn.

E. adnatum × palustre = E. × laschianum Hausskn.

8   E. lamyi F. W. Schultz

E. lamyi × parviflorum = E. × palatinum F. W. Schultz

E. lamyi × montanum = E. × haussknechtianum Borbás

E. lamyi × lanceolatum = E. × ambigens Hausskn.

E. lamyi × obscurum = E. × semiobscurum Borbás

9   E. obscurum Schreb.

E. obscurum × parviflorum = E. × dacicum Borbás

E. obscurum × roseum = E. × brachiatum Čelak.

E. obscurum × palustre = E. × schmidtianum Rostk.

10 E. palustre L.
    E. palustre × parviflorum = E. × rivulare Wahlenb.
    E. palustre × roseum = E. × purpureum Fr.
11 E. anagallidifolium Lam.
    E. alpinum auct.
    E. anagallidifolium × obscurum = E. × marshallianum Hausskn.
    E. anagallidifolium × palustre
    E. dasycarpum auct.
12 E. alsinifolium Vill.
    E. alsinifolium × montanum
    E. salicifolium Facch., non Stokes
    E. alsinifolium × obscurum = E. × rivulicola Hausskn.
    E. alsinifolium × palustre = E. × haynaldianum Hausskn.
    E. alsinifolium × anagallidifolium = E. × boissieri Hausskn.
13 *E. nerterioides Cunn.
    E. nummularifolium auct.; *E. pedunculare* auct.
14 *E. linnaeoides Hook. f.

255 CHAMAENERION Adans.

    1 C. angustifolium (L.) Scop.
        Epilobium angustifolium L.

256 *OENOTHERA L.

    1 *O. biennis L.
    2 *O. erythrosepala Borbás
        O. grandiflora auct.; *O. lamarkiana* auct.
    3 *O. stricta Ledeb. ex Link
        O. odorata auct.
    4 *O. parviflora L.
        O. muricata L.; *O. ammophila* Focke

257 *FUCHSIA L.

    1 *F. magellanica Lam.
        F. gracilis Lindl.; *F. riccartoni* auct.

258 CIRCAEA L.

    1 C. lutetiana L.
    2 C. intermedia Ehrh.
        C. canadensis auct.
    3 C. alpina L.

HALORAGACEAE

259 MYRIOPHYLLUM L.

    1 M. verticillatum L.
        M. pectinatum DC.
    2 M. spicatum L.
    3†*M. verrucosum Lindl.
    4 M. alterniflorum DC.
    5 *M. heterophyllum Michx.

260 *GUNNERA L.

    1 *G. tinctoria (Molina) Mirb.
        G. chilensis Lam.
    2 *G. manicata Linden ex André

HIPPURIDACEAE

261 HIPPURIS L.

    1 H. vulgaris L.

CALLITRICHACEAE

262 CALLITRICHE L.

    1 C. stagnalis Scop.
    2 C. platycarpa Kütz.
        C. polymorpha Lönnr.; *C. palustris* auct.; *C. verna*
        auct.; *C. vernalis* auct.
    3 C. obtusangula Le Gall
    4 C. intermedia Hoffm.
        C. pedunculata DC.; *C. hamulata* Kütz. ex Koch
    5 C. hermaphroditica L.
        C. autumnalis L.
    6 C. truncata Guss.

LORANTHACEAE

263 VISCUM L.

    1 V. album L.

SANTALACEAE

264 THESIUM L.

    1 T. humifusum DC.
        T. linophyllon auct.

CORNACEAE

265 THELYCRANIA (Dumort.) Fourr.
    1 T. sanguinea (L.) Fourr.
       Cornus sanguinea L.
    2 *T. sericea (L.) Dandy
       Cornus stolonifera Michx.

266 *CORNUS L.
    1 *C. mas L.

267 CHAMAEPERICLYMENUM Hill
    1 C. suecicum (L.) Aschers. & Graebn.
       Cornus suecica L.

ARALIACEAE

268 HEDERA L.
    1 H. helix L.

UMBELLIFERAE

269 HYDROCOTYLE L.
    1 H. vulgaris L.

270 SANICULA L.
    1 S. europaea L.

271 *ASTRANTIA L.
    1 *A. major L.

272 ERYNGIUM L.
    1 E. maritimum L.
    2 E. campestre L.

273 CHAEROPHYLLUM L.
    1 C. temulentum L.
    2 *C. aureum L.

274 ANTHRISCUS Pers.
    Cerefolium P. C. Fabr.
    1 A. caucalis Bieb.
       Chaerophyllum anthriscus (L.) Crantz; *Anthriscus vulgaris* Pers., non Bernh.; *A. neglecta* Boiss. &

UMBELLIFERAE

Reut.; *Cerefolium anthriscus* (L.) G. Beck;
Anthriscus scandicina Mansf.
2 A. sylvestris (L.) Hoffm.
Chaerophyllum sylvestre L.; *Cerefolium sylvestre*
(L.) Bess.
3 *A. cerefolium (L.) Hoffm.
Chaerophyllum cerefolium (L.) Crantz; *Cerefolium*
cerefolium (L.) Schinz & Thell.

275 SCANDIX L.
1 S. pecten-veneris L.

276 MYRRHIS Mill.
1 M. odorata (L.) Scop.

277 TORILIS Adans.
1 T. japonica (Houtt.) DC.
Caucalis anthriscus (L.) Huds.; *Torilis anthriscus*
(L.) C. C. Gmel., non Gaertn.
2 T. arvensis (Huds.) Link
Caucalis arvensis Huds.
3 T. nodosa (L.) Gaertn.
Caucalis nodosa (L.) Scop.

278 *CAUCALIS L.
1 *C. platycarpos L.
C. daucoides L. 1767, non L. 1753; *C. royeni* (L.)
Crantz; *C. lappula* Grande
2 *C. latifolia L.

279 *CORIANDRUM L.
1 *C. sativum L.

280 *SMYRNIUM L.
1 *S. olusatrum L.
2 *S. perfoliatum L.

281 PHYSOSPERMUM Cusson
Danaa All., non Sm.
1 P. cornubiense (L.) DC.
Danaa cornubiensis (L.) Burnat

282 CONIUM L.
1 C. maculatum L.

283 **BUPLEURUM** L.
    1 *B. fruticosum L.
    2 B. rotundifolium L.
    3 B. baldense Turra
         B. opacum (Ces.) Lange; *B. aristatum* auct.
    4 B. tenuissimum L.
    5 B. falcatum L.

284 **TRINIA** Hoffm.
    Apinella Baill.
    1 T. glauca (L.) Dumort.
         T. vulgaris DC.; *Apinella glauca* (L.) Caruel

285 **APIUM** L.
    1 A. graveolens L.
    2 A. nodiflorum (L.) Lag.
         A. nodiflorum × repens
    3 A. repens (Jacq.) Lag.
    4 A. inundatum (L.) Reichb. f.
         A. inundatum × nodiflorum = A. × moorei (Syme)
         Druce

286 **PETROSELINUM** Hill
    1 *P. crispum (Mill.) Nyman
         P. sativum Hoffm.; *Carum petroselinum* (L.) Benth.
    2 P. segetum (L.) Koch
         Carum segetum (L.) Benth. ex Hook. f.

287 **SISON** L.
    1 S. amomum L.

288 **CICUTA** L.
    1 C. virosa L.

289 ***AMMI** L.
    1 *A. majus L.

290 ***FALCARIA** Bernh.
    Prionitis Adans.
    1 *F. vulgaris Bernh.
         Prionitis falcaria (L.) Dumort.; *Falcaria falcaria*
         (L.) Karst.

291 CARUM L.
    1 C. verticillatum (L.) Koch
    2 C. carvi L.

292 BUNIUM L.
    1 B. bulbocastanum L.
         Carum bulbocastanum (L.) Koch

293 CONOPODIUM Koch
    1 C. majus (Gouan) Loret
         C. denudatum Koch; *Carum majus* (Gouan) Britten
         & Rendle

294 PIMPINELLA L.
    1 P. saxifraga L.
    2 P. major (L.) Huds.

295 *AEGOPODIUM L.
    1 *A. podagraria L.

296 SIUM L.
    1 S. latifolium L.

297 BERULA Koch
    1 B. erecta (Huds.) Coville
         Sium erectum Huds.; *S. angustifolium* L.

298 CRITHMUM L.
    1 C. maritimum L.

299 SESELI L.
    1 S. libanotis (L.) Koch

300 OENANTHE L.
    1 O. fistulosa L.
    2 O. pimpinelloides L.
    3 O. silaifolia Bieb.
         O. peucedanifolia auct.
    4 O. lachenalii C. C. Gmel.
    5 O. crocata L.
    6 O. aquatica (L.) Poir.
         O. phellandrium Lam.
    7 O. fluviatilis (Bab.) Colem.

UMBELLIFERAE

301 AETHUSA L.
1 A. cynapium L.

302 FOENICULUM Mill.
1 F. vulgare Mill.
F. officinale All.; *F. foeniculum* (L.) Karst.

303 SILAUM Mill.
Silaus Bernh.
1 S. silaus (L.) Schinz & Thell.
Silaus flavescens Bernh.; *S. pratensis* Bess.

304 MEUM Mill.
1 M. athamanticum Jacq.
M. meum (L.) Karst.

305 SELINUM L.
1 S. carvifolia (L.) L.

306 LIGUSTICUM L.
Haloscias Fr.
1 L. scoticum L.
Haloscias scotica (L.) Fr.

307 ANGELICA L.
Archangelica Hoffm.
1 A. sylvestris L.
2 *A. archangelica L.
Archangelica officinalis Hoffm.; *A. archangelica* (L.) Karst.

308 *LEVISTICUM Hill
1 *L. officinale Koch
L. levisticum (L.) Karst.

309 PEUCEDANUM L.
1 P. officinale L.
2 P. palustre (L.) Moench
3 *P. ostruthium (L.) Koch

310 PASTINACA L.
1 P. sativa L.
Peucedanum sativum (L.) Benth. ex Hook. f.

311 HERACLEUM L.

    1 H. sphondylium L.
    2 *H. mantegazzianum Somm. & Levier

312 *TORDYLIUM L.

    1 *T. maximum L.

313 *LASER Borkh.

    1 *L. trilobum (L.) Borkh.
        Siler trilobum (L.) Crantz

314 DAUCUS L.

    1 D. carota L.
    a subsp. carota
    b subsp. gummifer Hook. f.
        D. gummifer Lam., non All.; *D. gingidium* auct.

CUCURBITACEAE

315 BRYONIA L.

    1 B. dioica Jacq.

*ARISTOLOCHIACEAE

316 *ASARUM L.

    1 *A. europaeum L.

317 *ARISTOLOCHIA L.

    1 *A. clematitis L.
    2 *A. rotunda L.

EUPHORBIACEAE

318 MERCURIALIS L.

    1 M. perennis L.
    2 M. annua L.

319 EUPHORBIA L.

    1 E. peplis L.
    2 E. lathyrus L.
    3†*E. pilosa L.
    4 *E. corallioides L.
    5 E. hyberna L.

6 *E. dulcis L.
7 E. platyphyllos L.
8 E. stricta L.
9 E. helioscopia L.
10 E. peplus L.
11 E. exigua L.
12 E. portlandica L.
  E. segetalis auct.
13 E. paralias L.
14 *E. uralensis Fisch. ex Link
  E. virgata Waldst. & Kit., non Desf.
15 *E. esula L.
16 *E. cyparissias L.
17 E. amygdaloides L.
  E. turneri Druce

POLYGONACEAE

320 POLYGONUM L.

1 P. aviculare L. *sensu lato*

  1 P. aviculare L.
    P. heterophyllum Lindm.
  2 P. littorale Link
  3 P. rurivagum Jord. ex Bor.
  4 P. aequale Lindm.
  5 P. calcatum Lindm.
  6 P. microspermum Jord. ex Bor.

2 P. raii Bab.
  P. roberti auct.
3 P. maritimum L.
4 *P. cognatum Meisn.
5 P. viviparum L.
6 P. bistorta L.
7 *P. amplexicaule D. Don
8 P. amphibium L.
9 P. persicaria L.
10 P. lapathifolium L.
  P. scabrum Moench
  P. lapathifolium × persicaria = P. × lenticulare Hy
11 P. nodosum Pers.
  P. maculatum (Gray) Dyer ex Bab.; *P. petecticale* (Stokes) Druce; *P. laxum* auct.

POLYGONACEAE

12 P. hydropiper L.
   P. hydropiper × persicaria = P. × intercedens G. Beck
   P. hydropiper × nodosum = P. × metschii G. Beck
   P. hydropiper × mite
   P. hydropiper × minus = P. × subglandulosum Borbás
13 P. mite Schrank
       P. laxiflorum Weihe
     P. mite × persicaria = P. × condensatum (F. W. Schultz)
       F. W. Schultz
14 P. minus Huds.
   P. minus × persicaria = P. × braunianum F. W. Schultz
   P. minus × mite = P. × wilmsii G. Beck
15 P. convolvulus L.
16 P. dumetorum L.
17 *P. sagittatum L.
18 *P. baldschuanicum Regel
19 *P. cuspidatum Sieb. & Zucc.
       P. compactum Hook. f.
20 *P. sachalinense F. Schmidt
21 *P. polystachyum Wall. ex Meisn.
22 *P. campanulatum Hook. f.

321 *FAGOPYRUM Mill.
   1 *F. esculentum Moench
       Polygonum fagopyrum L.; *Fagopyrum sagittatum*
       Gilib.; *F. fagopyrum* (L.) Karst.

322 KOENIGIA L.
   1 K. islandica L.

323 *MUEHLENBECKIA Meisn.
   1 *M. complexa (Cunn.) Meisn.

324 OXYRIA Hill
   1 O. digyna (L.) Hill

325 RUMEX L.
   1 R. acetosella L. *sensu lato*
       1 R. acetosella L.
       2 R. angiocarpus Murb.
       3 R. tenuifolius (Wallr.) Löve
   2 R. acetosa L.
   3 *R. scutatus L.

4 R. hydrolapathum Huds.
   R. hydrolapathum × obtusifolius = R. × weberi Fisch.-
   Benz.
   R. maximus auct.; *R. heterophyllus* auct.
5 *R. alpinus L.
6 *R. confertus Willd.
   R. confertus × crispus = R. × skofitzii Blocki
   R. confertus × obtusifolius = R × borbasii Blocki
7 R. aquaticus L.
   R. aquaticus × obtusifolius = R. × schmidtii Hausskn.
8 R. longifolius DC.
   R. domesticus Hartm.; *R. aquaticus* auct.
   R. longifolius × obtusifolius = R. × arnottii Druce
   R. conspersus auct.
9 *R. cristatus DC.
   R. graecus Boiss. & Heldr.
10 *R. patientia L.
   a *subsp. patientia
   b *subsp. orientalis (Bernh.) Danser
11 R. crispus L.
   R. elongatus Guss.
   R. crispus × longifolius = R. × propinquus Aresch.
   R. crispus × cristatus
   R. crispus × patientia
   R. crispus × obtusifolius = R. × acutus L.
   R. pratensis Mert. & Koch
   R. crispus × pulcher = R. × pseudopulcher Hausskn.
   R. crispus × sanguineus = R. × sagorskii Hausskn.
   R. crispus × rupestris
12 R. obtusifolius L.
   a subsp. obtusifolius
   b *subsp. transiens (Simonk.) Reching. f.
   c *subsp. sylvestris (Wallr.) Reching.
   R. obtusifolius × patientia = R. × erubescens Simonk.
   R. obtusifolius × pulcher = R. × ogulinensis Borbás
   R. obtusifolius × sanguineus = R. × dufftii Hausskn.
   R. obtusifolius × palustris = R. × steinii Becker
13 R. pulcher L.
   R. pulcher × sanguineus
   R. pulcher × rupestris = R. × trimenii Camus
14 R. sanguineus L.
   R. condylodes Bieb.; *R. nemorosus* Schrad. ex Willd.;
   R. viridis (Sibth.) Druce

15 R. conglomeratus Murr.
    R. glomeratus Schreb.
    R. conglomeratus × hydrolapathum = R. × digeneus G. Beck
    R. conglomeratus × crispus = R. × schulzei Hausskn.
    R. conglomeratus × obtusifolius = R. × abortivus Ruhmer
    R. conglomeratus × pulcher = R. × muretii Hausskn.
    R. conglomeratus × sanguineus = R. × ruhmeri Hausskn.
    R. varians Druce
    R. conglomeratus × palustris
    R. conglomeratus × maritimus = R. × knafii Čelak.
    R. conglomeratus × frutescens = R. × wrightii Lousley
16 R. rupestris Le Gall
17 R. palustris Sm.
    R. limosus auct.
18 R. maritimus L.
    R. maritimus × obtusifolius = R. × callianthemus Danser
19 *R. brownii Campd.
20 *R. frutescens Thou.
    R. cuneifolius Campd.; *R. magellanicus* auct.
21 *R. triangulivalvis (Danser) Reching. f.
    R. salicifolius auct.

URTICACEAE

326 PARIETARIA L.
    1 P. diffusa Mert. & Koch
       P. officinalis auct.; *P. ramiflora* auct.

327 *HELXINE Req.
    1 *H. soleirolii Req.

328 URTICA L.
    1 U. urens L.
    2 U. dioica L.
       U. hispida DC.
    3†*U. pilulifera L.
       U. dodartii L.

CANNABIACEAE
329 HUMULUS L.
    1 H. lupulus L.

ULMACEAE
330 ULMUS L.
    1 U. glabra Huds.
        U. scabra Mill.; *U. montana* Stokes
        U. glabra × plotii=U. × elegantissima Horwood
    2 U. procera Salisb.
        U. anglica Druce; *U. campestris* auct.; *U. sativa*
        auct.
    3 U. angustifolia (Weston) Weston
        U. stricta (Ait.) Lindl.; *U. minor* auct.
        U. angustifolia × glabra
    4 U. coritana Melville
        U. coritana × glabra=U. × hollandica Mill.
        U. major Sm.
        U. coritana × plotii
        U. coritana × ?=U. × diversifolia Melville
    5 U. carpinifolia Gled.
        U. nitens Moench
        U. carpinifolia × glabra=U. × vegeta (Loud.) A. Ley
        U. carpinifolia × plotii
    6 U. plotii Druce
        U. minor auct.

*MORACEAE
331 *FICUS L.
    1 *F. carica L.

*JUGLANDACEAE
332 *JUGLANS L.
    1 *J. regia L.

MYRICACEAE
333 MYRICA L.
    1 M. gale L.
    2 *M. caroliniensis Mill.
        M. pensylvanica Lois.

*PLATANACEAE

334 *PLATANUS L.
1 *P. × hybrida Brot.
   P. acerifolia (Ait.) Willd.

BETULACEAE
335 BETULA L.
1 B. pendula Roth
   B. verrucosa Ehrh.; *B. alba* auct.
   B. pendula × pubescens = B. × aurata Borkh.
   B. hybrida Bechst., non Blom
2 B. pubescens Ehrh.
   a   subsp. pubescens
   b   subsp. odorata (Bechst.) E. F. Warb.
3 B. nana L.
   B. nana × pubescens = B. × intermedia Thomas ex Gaudin
   B. alpestris Fr.

336 ALNUS Mill.
1 A. glutinosa (L.) Gaertn.
   A. rotundifolia Stokes; *A. alnus* (L.) Britton
   A. glutinosa × incana = A. × pubescens Tausch
2 *A. incana (L.) Moench

CORYLACEAE
337 CARPINUS L.
1 C. betulus L.

338 CORYLUS L.
1 C. avellana L.

FAGACEAE
339 FAGUS L.
1 F. sylvatica L.

340 *CASTANEA Mill.
1 *C. sativa Mill.
   C. castanea (L.) Karst.

341 QUERCUS L.

    1 *Q. cerris L.
    2 *Q. ilex L.
    3 Q. robur L.
    4 Q. petraea (Mattuschka) Liebl.
       Q. sessiliflora Salisb.
       Q. petraea × robur = Q. × rosacea Bechst.
       Q. intermedia Boenn. ex Reichb.

SALICACEAE

342 POPULUS L.

    1 *P. alba L.
    2 P. canescens (Ait.) Sm.
       P. canescens × tremula = P. × hybrida Bieb.
    3 P. tremula L.
    4 P. nigra L.
    5 *P. × canadensis Moench
       P. serotina Hartig; *P. lloydii* Henry; *P. deltoides* auct.
    6 *P. gileadensis Rouleau
       P. balsamifera auct.; *P. tacamahacca* auct.

343 SALIX L.

    1 S. pentandra L.
    2 S. alba L.
       S. alba × pentandra = S. × ehrhartiana Sm.
       S. hexandra auct.
      *S. alba × babylonica = S. × sepulcralis Simonk.
       S. alba × fragilis = S. × rubens Schrank
       S. alba var. *caerulea* (Sm.) Sm.; *S. viridis* auct.
    3 *S. babylonica L.
      *S. babylonica × fragilis = S. × blanda Anderss.
    4 S. fragilis L.
       S. decipiens Hoffm.; *S. russelliana* Sm.
       S. fragilis × pentandra = S. × meyerana Rostk. ex Willd.
       S. cuspidata K. F. Schultz
       S. fragilis × triandra = S. × speciosa Host
       S. alopecuroides (Reichb.) A. Kerner
    5 S. triandra L.
       S. triandra × viminalis = S. × mollissima Ehrh.
       S. undulata Ehrh.; *S. hippophaefolia* Thuill.; *S. lanceolata* Sm.

6 S. purpurea L.
   S. purpurea × viminalis = S. × rubra Huds.
   S. purpurea × repens = S. × doniana Sm.
7 *S. daphnoides Vill.
8 *S. acutifolia Willd.
   S. pruinosa Wendl. ex Reichb.; *S. daphnoides* subsp.
     acutifolia (Willd.) Zahn
9 S. viminalis L.
   S. viminalis × ? = S. × stipularis Sm.
10 *S. calodendron Wimm.
   S. dasyclados auct.; *S. acuminata* auct.
   S. calodendron × purpurea = S. × taylorii Reching. f.
11 S. caprea L.
  a   subsp. caprea
  b   subsp. sericea (Anderss.) Flod.
      S. coaetanea (Hartm.) Flod.
   S. caprea × viminalis = S. × laurina Sm.
   S. sericans Tausch ex A. Kerner
   S. caprea × cinerea = S. × reichardtii A. Kerner
   S. caprea × cinerea × viminalis
   S. caprea × nigricans = S. × latifolia Forbes
   S. caprea × nigricans × phylicifolia
   S. caprea × phylicifolia
   S. bicolor auct.
   S. caprea × repens = S. × laschiana Zahn
   S. caprea × lapponum = S. × laestadiana Hartm.
   S. caprea × lanata = S. × balfourii E. F. Linton
   S. caprea × myrsinites = S. × lintonii G. & A. Camus
12 S. cinerea L.
  a   subsp. cinerea
  b   subsp. atrocinerea (Brot.) Silva & Sobrinho
      S. atrocinerea Brot.
   S. cinerea × purpurea = S. × sordida A. Kerner
   S. cinerea × purpurea × viminalis = S. × forbyana Sm.
   S. cinerea × viminalis = S. × smithiana Willd.
   S. geminata Forbes; *S. chouardii* Chass. & Görz
   S. cinerea × nigricans = S. × strepida Forbes
   S. cinerea × nigricans × phylicifolia
   S. cinerea × phylicifolia = S. × wardiana Leefe ex F. B.
    White
   S. cinerea × repens = S. × subsericea Doell
   S. cinerea × repens × viminalis = S. × angusensis Reching. f.

SALICACEAE

13   S. aurita L.

       S. aurita × purpurea = S. × dichroa Doell

       S. aurita × viminalis = S. × fruticosa Doell

       S. aurita × caprea = S. × capreola J. Kerner ex Anderss.

       S. aurita × cinerea = S. × multinervis Doell

       S. lutescens A. Kerner

       S. aurita × cinerea × purpurea = S. × confinis G. & A. Camus

       S. aurita × cinerea × nigricans = S. × forbesiana Druce

       S. waldsteiniana auct.

       S. aurita × cinerea × phylicifolia

       S. aurita × cinerea × repens

       S. aurita × nigricans = S. × coriacea Forbes

       S. aurita × nigricans × phylicifolia = S. × saxetana F. B. White

       S. aurita × phylicifolia = S. × ludificans F. B. White

       S. aurita × phylicifolia × purpurea = S. × sesquitertia F. B. White

       S. aurita × repens = S. × ambigua Ehrh.

       S. aurita × lapponum = S. × obtusifolia Willd.

       S. aurita × myrsinites

       S. aurita × myrsinites × nigricans

       S. aurita × herbacea = S. × margarita F. B. White

14   S. nigricans Sm.

       S. andersoniana Sm.

       S. nigricans × phylicifolia = S. × tetrapla Walker

       S. fraserii Druce

       S. nigricans × repens

15   S. phylicifolia L.

       S. phylicifolia × purpurea = S. × secerneta F. B. White

       S. phylicifolia × repens = S. × schraderana Willd.

16   S. repens L.

    a   subsp. repens

           S. rosmarinifolia auct.

    b   subsp. argentea (Sm.) G. & A. Camus

           S. arenaria auct.

       S. repens × viminalis = S. × friesiana Anderss.

17   S. lapponum L.

       S. lapponum × phylicifolia = S. × gillotii G. & A. Camus

       S. lapponum × repens = S. × pithoensis Rouy

       S. subversifolia G. & A. Camus

       S. lapponum × myrsinites = S. × phaeophylla Anderss.

       S. lapponum × reticulata = S. × boydii E. F. Linton

18   S. lanata L.
      S. lanata × lapponum
      S. lanata × reticulata
19   S. arbuscula L.
      S. arbuscula × nigricans
       S. kraettliana auct.
      S. arbuscula × nigricans × phylicifolia
      S. arbuscula × phylicifolia
       S. dicksoniana auct.
      S. arbuscula × lapponum = S. × pseudospuria Rouy
       S. whiteana G. & A. Camus; *S. spuria* auct.
      S. arbuscula × herbacea = S. × simulatrix F. B. White
20   S. myrsinites L.
      S. myrsinites × nigricans = S. × punctata Wahlenb.
       S. macnabiana Macgill.
      S. myrsinites × nigricans × phylicifolia
      S. myrsinites × phylicifolia = S. × notha Anderss.
21   S. herbacea L.
      S. herbacea × phylicifolia = S. × moorei F. B. White
      S. herbacea × repens = S. × cernua E. F. Linton
      S. herbacea × lapponum = S. × sobrina F. B. White
       S. ovata Ser., non Spreng.
      S. herbacea × lapponum × myrsinites = S. × eugenes E.
       F. Linton
      S. herbacea × lanata = S. × sadleri Syme
      S. herbacea × myrsinites = S. × grahamii Borrer ex Bak.
      S. herbacea × reticulata
22   S. reticulata L.

ERICACEAE

344 LEDUM L.

  1   L. palustre L.
  2 *L. groenlandicum Oeder
      L. latifolium Jacq.

345 *RHODODENDRON L.

  1 *R. ponticum L.
  2 *R. luteum Sweet

346 LOISELEURIA Desv.

  1   L. procumbens (L.) Desv.
      Azalea procumbens L.

ERICACEAE

347 *KALMIA L.
    1 *K. polifolia Wangenh.
       K. glauca L'Hérit. ex Ait.

348 PHYLLODOCE Salisb.
    1 P. caerulea (L.) Bab.
       Menziesia caerulea (L.) Sw.; *Bryanthus caeruleus*
       (L.) Dippel

349 DABOECIA D. Don
    Boretta Baill.
    1 D. cantabrica (Huds.) C. Koch
       Menziesia polyfolia Juss.; *Daboecia polifolia* D. Don;
       Boretta cantabrica (Huds.) Kuntze

350 ANDROMEDA L.
    1 A. polifolia L.

351 *GAULTHERIA L.
    1 *G. shallon Pursh
    2 *G. procumbens L.

352 *PERNETTYA Gaudich.
    1 *P. mucronata (L. f.) Gaudich. ex Spreng.

353 ARBUTUS L.
    1 A. unedo L.

354 ARCTOSTAPHYLOS Adans.
    1 A. uva-ursi (L.) Spreng.

355 ARCTOUS (A. Gray) Nied.
    1 A. alpinus (L.) Nied.
       Arctostaphylos alpinus (L.) Spreng.

356 CALLUNA Salisb.
    1 C. vulgaris (L.) Hull

357 ERICA L.
    1 E. tetralix L.
       E. tetralix×vagans=E.×williamsii Druce
    2 E. mackaiana Bab.
       E. mackaii Hook.

E. mackaiana × tetralix = E. × stuartii E. F. Linton
E. praegeri Ostenf.
3 E. ciliaris L.
E. ciliaris × tetralix = E. × watsonii Benth.
4 E. cinerea L.
5 *E. terminalis Salisb.
6 *E. lusitanica Rudolphi
7 E. mediterranea L.
E. hibernica (Hook. & Arn.) Syme; *E. carnea* auct.
8 E. vagans L.

358 **VACCINIUM L.**
Oxycoccus Hill
1 V. vitis-idaea L.
2 V. myrtillus L.
V. myrtillus × vitis-idaea = V. × intermedium Ruthe
3 V. uliginosum L.
4 V. oxycoccos L.
Oxycoccus quadripetalus Gilib.; *O. palustris* Pers.;
O. oxycoccos (L.) MacMill.
5 V. microcarpum (Rupr.) Hook. f.
Oxycoccus microcarpus Turcz. ex Rupr.
6 *V. macrocarpon Ait.
Oxycoccus macrocarpos (Ait.) Pursh

PYROLACEAE
359 **PYROLA L.**
1 P. minor L.
P. redgrovensis Druce
2 P. media Sw.
3 P. rotundifolia L.
a subsp. rotundifolia
b subsp. maritima (Kenyon) E. F. Warb.

360 **ORTHILIA Raf.**
Ramischia Opiz ex Garcke
1 O. secunda (L.) House
Pyrola secunda L.; *Ramischia secunda* (L.) Garcke

361 **MONESES Salisb.**
1 M. uniflora (L.) A. Gray
Pyrola uniflora L.

MONOTROPACEAE

362 MONOTROPA L.
> *Hypopitys* Hill
> 1 M. hypopitys L. *sensu lato*
>> *1* M. hypopitys L.
>> *Hypopitys multiflora* Scop.; *H. hypopitys* (L.) Small
>> 2 M. hypophegea Wallr.

DIAPENSIACEAE

363 DIAPENSIA L.
> 1 D. lapponica L.

EMPETRACEAE

364 EMPETRUM L.
> 1 E. nigrum L.
> 2 E. hermaphroditum Hagerup

PLUMBAGINACEAE

365 LIMONIUM Mill.
> 1 L. vulgare Mill.
> *Statice limonium* L.; *Limonium limonium* (L.) A. B. Lyons
> 2 L. humile Mill.
> *Statice rariflora* Drej.; *S. humilis* (Mill.) C. E. Salmon, non Link
> L. humile×vulgare=L.×neumanii C. E. Salmon
> 3 L. bellidifolium (Gouan) Dumort.
> *L. reticulatum* Mill. *pro parte*; *Statice bellidifolia* (Gouan) DC.
> 4 [L. auriculae-ursifolium (Pourr.) Druce
> *Statice lychnidifolia* Girard; *Limonium lychnidifolium* Kuntze]
> 5 L. binervosum (G. E. Sm.) C. E. Salmon *sensu lato*
> *Statice binervosa* G. E. Sm.
>> *1* L. binervosum (G. E. Sm.) C. E. Salmon
>> *Statice auriculaefolia* auct.
>> *2* L. recurvum C. E. Salmon
>> *Statice recurva* (C. E. Salmon) C. E. Salmon; *S. dodartii* auct.
>> *3* L. transwallianum (Pugsl.) Pugsl.
>> *4* L. paradoxum Pugsl.

366 ARMERIA Willd.
Statice L.

1 A. maritima (Mill.) Willd.
   Statice armeria L.; *S. maritima* Mill.
   a subsp. maritima
        Armeria vulgaris Willd.; *A. pubescens* Link;
        Statice pubescens (Link) Druce, non DC.;
        S. planifolia (Syme) Druce
   b subsp. elongata (Hoffm.) Bonnier
2 [A. arenaria (Pers.) Schult.
   Statice plantaginea All.; *Armeria plantaginea* Willd.]
   [A. arenaria × maritima]
3 *A. pseudarmeria (Murr.) Lawrence
   A. latifolia Willd.

PRIMULACEAE

367 PRIMULA L.

1 P. farinosa L.
2 P. scotica Hook.
3 P. veris L.
   P. veris × vulgaris
   P. variabilis Goupil, non Bast.
4 P. elatior (L.) Hill
   P. elatior × veris = P. × media Peterm.
   P. elatior × vulgaris = P. × digenea A. Kerner
5 P. vulgaris Huds.
   P. acaulis (L.) Hill

368 HOTTONIA L.

1 H. palustris L.

369 *CYCLAMEN L.

1 *C. hederifolium Ait.
   C. neapolitanum Ten.; *C. europaeum* auct.

370 LYSIMACHIA L.
Naumburgia Moench; *Steironema* Raf.

1 L. nemorum L.
2 L. nummularia L.
3 L. vulgaris L.

4 *L. ciliata L.
   Steironema ciliatum (L.) Baudo
5 *L. punctata L.
6 *L. terrestris (L.) Britton, Sterns & Poggenb.
7 L. thyrsiflora L.
   Naumburgia thyrsiflora (L.) Reichb.

371 TRIENTALIS L.
  1 T. europaea L.

372 ANAGALLIS L.
   Centunculus L.
  1 A. tenella (L.) L.
  2 A. arvensis L.
   A. arvensis × foemina
  3 A. foemina Mill.
   A. caerulea Schreb., non L.; *A. arvensis* subsp.
   foemina (Mill.) Schinz & Thell.
  4 A. minima (L.) E. H. L. Krause
   Centunculus minimus L.

373 GLAUX L.
  1 G. maritima L.

374 SAMOLUS L.
  1 S. valerandi L.

*BUDDLEJACEAE

375 *BUDDLEJA L.
  1 *B. davidii Franch.

OLEACEAE

376 FRAXINUS L.
  1 F. excelsior L.

377 *SYRINGA L.
  1 *S. vulgaris L.

378 LIGUSTRUM L.
  1 L. vulgare L.
  2 *L. ovalifolium Hassk.

APOCYNACEAE

379 VINCA L.

1 V. minor L.
2 *V. major L.
3 *V. herbacea Waldst. & Kit.

GENTIANACEAE

380 CICENDIA Adans.
Microcala Hoffmanns. & Link

1 C. filiformis (L.) Delarb.
Microcala filiformis (L.) Hoffmanns. & Link

381 [EXACULUM Caruel]

1 [E. pusillum (Lam.) Caruel
Cicendia pusilla (Lam.) Griseb.]

382 CENTAURIUM Hill
Erythraea Borkh.

1 C. pulchellum (Sw.) Druce
Erythraea pulchella (Sw.) Fr.
2 C. tenuiflorum (Hoffmanns. & Link) Fritsch
Erythraea tenuiflora Hoffmanns. & Link
3 †C. latifolium (Sm.) Druce
Erythraea latifolia Sm.
4 C. erythraea Rafn
C. centaurium Druce *pro parte*; *C. minus* auct.;
C. umbellatum auct.; *Erythraea centaurium* auct.
C. erythraea × pulchellum
C. erythraea × littorale = C. intermedium (Wheldon)
Druce
5 C. capitatum (Willd.) Borbás
Erythraea capitata Willd.
6 C. littorale (D. Turner) Gilmour
C. vulgare Rafn; *Erythraea compressa* Kunth;
E. littoralis (D. Turner) Fr.; *E. turneri* Wheldon
& Salmon
7 C. scilloides (L. f.) Samp.
Erythraea portensis (Brot.) Hoffmanns. & Link;
Centaurium portense (Brot.) Butcher

89

383 **BLACKSTONIA** Huds.
    Chlora Adans.
    1 B. perfoliata (L.) Huds.
       Chlora perfoliata (L.) L.

384 **GENTIANA** L.
    1 G. pneumonanthe L.
    2 G. verna L.
    3 G. nivalis L.

385 **GENTIANELLA** Moench
    1 G. campestris (L.) Börner
       Gentiana campestris L.; *G. baltica* auct.; *Gentian-
       ella baltica* auct.
    2 G. germanica (Willd.) Börner
       Gentiana germanica Willd.
    3 G. amarella (L.) Börner *sensu lato*
       Gentiana amarella L.
       1 G. amarella (L.) Börner
       2 G. septentrionalis (Druce) E. F. Warb.
           Gentiana septentrionalis (Druce) Druce
       G. amarella × germanica = G. × pamplinii (Druce) E.
       F. Warb.
       Gentiana pamplinii Druce
       G. amarella × uliginosa
    4 G. anglica (Pugsl.) E. F. Warb.
       Gentiana lingulata var. *praecox* (Townsend) Wettst.;
       G. anglica Pugsl.
    5 G. uliginosa (Willd.) Börner
       Gentiana uliginosa Willd.

MENYANTHACEAE

386 **MENYANTHES** L.
    1 M. trifoliata L.

387 **NYMPHOIDES** Hill
    Limnanthemum S. G. Gmel.
    1 N. peltata (S. G. Gmel.) Kuntze
       Limnanthemum peltatum S. G. Gmel.; *Nymphoides
       orbiculata* Gilib.; *Limnanthemum nymphoides* (L.)
       Hoffmanns. & Link; *Nymphoides nymphoides*
       (L.) Druce

POLEMONIACEAE

388 POLEMONIUM L.
 1 P. caeruleum L.

BORAGINACEAE

389 CYNOGLOSSUM L.
 1 C. officinale L.
 2 C. germanicum Jacq.
    C. montanum auct.

390 *OMPHALODES Mill.
 1 *O. verna Moench
    O. omphaloides (L.) Voss

391 *ASPERUGO L.
 1 *A. procumbens L.

392 SYMPHYTUM L.
 1 S. officinale L.
 2 *S. asperum Lepech.
    S. asperrimum Donn ex Sims
   *S. asperum × officinale = S. × uplandicum Nyman
    S. peregrinum auct.; *S. lilacinum* auct.; *S. densi-
    florum* auct.; *S. caeruleum* auct.
 3 *S. orientale L.
 4 *S. caucasicum Bieb.
 5 *S. tauricum Willd.
 6 S. tuberosum L.
 7 *S. grandiflorum DC.

393 *BORAGO L.
 1 *B. officinalis L.
 2 *B. laxiflora Willd.

394 *TRACHYSTEMON D. Don
 1 *T. orientalis (L.) G. Don

395 *PENTAGLOTTIS Tausch
 1 *P. sempervirens (L.) Tausch
    Anchusa sempervirens L.

91

BORAGINACEAE

396 *ANCHUSA L.
    1 *A. officinalis L.
    2 *A. ochroleuca Bieb.
    3 *A. azurea Mill.

397 LYCOPSIS L.
    1   L. arvensis L.
        Anchusa arvensis (L.) Bieb.

398 *NONEA Medic.
    1 *N. rosea (Bieb.) Link

399 PULMONARIA L.
    1   P. longifolia (Bast.) Bor.
        P. angustifolia auct.
    2 *P. officinalis L.

400 MYOSOTIS L.
    1   M. scorpioides L.
        M. palustris (L.) Hill
    2   M. secunda A. Murr.
        M. repens auct.
    3   M. brevifolia C. E. Salmon
    4   M. caespitosa K. F. Schultz
    5   [M. sicula Guss.]
    6   M. alpestris Schmidt
        M. pyrenaica auct.
    7   M. sylvatica Hoffm.
    8   M. arvensis (L.) Hill
    9   M. discolor Pers.
        M. versicolor Sm.
   10   M. ramosissima Rochel
        M. hispida Schlecht.; *M. collina* auct.

401 LITHOSPERMUM L.
    1   L. purpurocaeruleum L.
    2   L. officinale L.
    3   L. arvense L.

402 MERTENSIA Roth
    Pneumaria Hill
    1   M. maritima (L.) Gray
        Pneumaria maritima (L.) Hill

403 ECHIUM L.
　1　E. vulgare L.
　2　E. lycopsis L.
　　　E. plantagineum L.

CONVOLVULACEAE

404 *DICHONDRA J. R. & G. Forst.
　1　*D. repens J. R. & G. Forst.

405 CONVOLVULUS L.
　1　C. arvensis L.

406 CALYSTEGIA R.Br.
　　　Volvulus Medic.
　1　C. sepium (L.) R.Br.
　　　Convolvulus sepium L.; *Volvulus sepium* (L.) Junger
　　　C. sepium × silvatica
　2　*C. dahurica (Herbert) G. Don
　　　Volvulus dahuricus (Herbert) Junger
　3　*C. silvatica (Kit.) Griseb.
　　　C. sylvestris (Willd.) Roem. & Schult.; *Volvulus
　　　　inflatus* Druce *pro parte*; *Calystegia inflata* auct.
　4　C. soldanella (L.) R.Br.
　　　Convolvulus soldanella L.; *Volvulus soldanella* (L.)
　　　Junger

407 CUSCUTA L.
　1　C. europaea L.
　2　*C. epilinum Weihe
　3　C. epithymum (L.) L.
　　　C. trifolii Bab.

SOLANACEAE

408 *NICANDRA Adans.
　1　*N. physalodes (L.) Gaertn.

409 *LYCIUM L.
　1　*L. halimifolium Mill.
　2　*L. chinense Mill.
　　　L. barbarum auct.

410 ATROPA L.

    1 A. bella-donna L.

411 HYOSCYAMUS L.

    1 H. niger L.

412 *PHYSALIS L.

    1 *P. alkekengi L.

413 SOLANUM L.

    1 S. dulcamara L.
    2 *S. pseudocapsicum L.
    3 S. nigrum L.
    4 *S. sarrachoides Sendtn.
        S. nitidibaccatum Bitter; *S. chenopodioides* auct.
    5 *S. triflorum Nutt.

414 *SALPICHROA Miers

    1 *S. origanifolia (Lam.) Baill.

415 *DATURA L.

    1 *D. stramonium L.
        D. tatula L.; *D. inermis* Juss. ex Jacq.

SCROPHULARIACEAE

416 VERBASCUM L.

    1 V. thapsus L.
        V. schraderi G. F. W. Mey.
    2 *V. thapsiforme Schrad.
    3 *V. phlomoides L.
        V. phlomoides × thapsus
    4 V. lychnitis L.
        V. lychnitis × thapsus = V. × thapsi L.
        V. foliosum Franch.
        V. lychnitis × pulverulentum = V. × regelianum Wirtg.
        V. pulvinatum auct.
        V. lychnitis × nigrum = V. × schiedeanum Koch
    5 V. pulverulentum Vill.
        V. floccosum Waldst. & Kit.
        V. pulverulentum × thapsus = V. × godronii Bor.
        V. lamottei Franch.

6 *V. speciosum Schrad.
7 V. nigrum L.
  V. nigrum × thapsus = V. × semialbum Chaub.
  V. collinum Schrad., non Salisb.
  V. nigrum × pulverulentum = V. × wirtgenii Franch.
  V. schottianum auct.
8 *V. chaixii Vill.
  V. austriacum Schott ex Roem. & Schult.
9 *V. blattaria L.
10 V. virgatum Stokes

417 MISOPATES Raf.
  1 M. orontium (L.) Raf.
    Antirrhinum orontium L.

418 *ANTIRRHINUM L.
  1 *A. majus L.

419 *ASARINA Mill.
  1 *A. procumbens Mill.
    Antirrhinum asarina L.

420 LINARIA Mill.
  1 [L. pelisseriana (L.) Mill.]
  2 *L. purpurea (L.) Mill.
    L. purpurea × repens = L. × dominii Druce
  3 L. repens (L.) Mill.
    L. repens × vulgaris = L. × sepium Allman
    L. repens × supina = L. × cornubiensis Druce
  4 L. vulgaris Mill.
    L. linaria (L.) Karst.
  5 *L. dalmatica (L.) Mill.
  6 *L. supina (L.) Chazelles
  7 *L. arenaria DC.

421 CHAENORHINUM (DC.) Reichb.
  1 C. minus (L.) Lange
    Linaria minor (L.) Desf.
  2 *C. origanifolium (L.) Fourr.
    Linaria origanifolia (L.) DC.

422 KICKXIA Dumort.

    1 K. spuria (L.) Dumort.
       Linaria spuria (L.) Mill.
    2 K. elatine (L.) Dumort.
       Linaria elatine (L.) Mill.

423 *CYMBALARIA Hill

    1 *C. muralis Gaertn., Mey. & Scherb.
       Linaria cymbalaria (L.) Mill.
    2 *C. pallida (Ten.) Wettst.
       Linaria pallida (Ten.) Guss.

424 SCROPHULARIA L.

    1 S. nodosa L.
    2 S. aquatica L.
    3 S. umbrosa Dumort.
       S. alata Gilib.; *S. ehrharti* Stevens; *S. hurstii* Druce;
       S. towndrowi Druce
    4 S. scorodonia L.
    5 *S. vernalis L.

425 *MIMULUS L.

    1 *M. guttatus DC.
       M. langsdorffii Donn ex Greene; *M. luteus* auct.
    2 *M. luteus L.
    3 *M. moschatus Dougl. ex Lindl.

426 LIMOSELLA L.

    1 L. aquatica L.
       L. aquatica × subulata
    2 L. subulata Ives

427 SIBTHORPIA L.

    1 S. europaea L.

428 *ERINUS L.

    1 *E. alpinus L.

429 DIGITALIS L.

    1 D. purpurea L.
    2 *D. lanata Ehrh.

430 VERONICA L.

1   V. beccabunga L.
2   V. anagallis-aquatica L.
    V. anagallis-aquatica × catenata
3   V. catenata Pennell
    V. aquatica Bernh., non Gray
4   V. scutellata L.
5   V. officinalis L.
6   V. montana L.
7   V. chamaedrys L.
8   V. spicata L.
   a   subsp. spicata
   b   subsp. hybrida (L.) E. F. Warb.
       V. hybrida L.
9 *V. longifolia L.
10   V. fruticans Jacq.
    V. saxatilis Scop.
11 *V. repens Clarion ex DC.
12   V. alpina L.
13   V. serpyllifolia L.
   a   subsp. serpyllifolia
   b   subsp. humifusa (Dickson) Syme
       V. humifusa Dickson
14 *V. peregrina L.
15   V. arvensis L.
16   V. verna L.
17 *V. acinifolia L.
18 *V. praecox All.
19   V. triphyllos L.
20   V. hederifolia L.
21 *V. persica Poir.
    V. buxbaumii Ten., non Schmidt; *V. tournefortii* auct.
22   V. polita Fr.
    V. didyma auct.
23   V. agrestis L.
24 *V. filiformis Sm.
25 *V. crista-galli Stev.

431 *HEBE Commers.

1 *H. lewisii (Armstrong) Cockayne & Allan
    Veronica lewisii Armstrong
2 *H. salicifolia (Forst. f.) Pennell
    Veronica salicifolia Forst. f.

432 PEDICULARIS L.

    1 P. palustris L.
    2 P. sylvatica L.

433 RHINANTHUS L.

    1 R. serotinus (Schönh.) Oborny
        R. major Ehrh., non L.; *R. apterus* (Fr.) Ostenf.; *R. borbasii* (Dörfl.) Soó; *R. aestivalis* (Zinger) Clapham; *R. polycladus* (Chabert) Clapham
    2 R. minor L.
        R. drummond-hayi (F. B. White) Druce; *R. gardineri* Druce; *R. calcareus* Wilmott; *R. spadiceus* Wilmott; *R. lintoni* Wilmott; *R. lochabrensis* Wilmott; *R. vachellae* Wilmott; *R. crista-galli* auct.; *R. borealis* auct.; *R. groenlandicus* auct.; *R. monticola* auct.; *R. perrieri* auct.; *R. rusticulus* auct.; *R. stenophyllus* auct.
        R. minor × serotinus

434 MELAMPYRUM L.

    1 M. cristatum L.
    2 M. arvense L.
    3 M. pratense L.
        M. vulgatum Pers.
    4 M. sylvaticum L.

435 EUPHRASIA L.

    1 E. officinalis L. *sensu lato*

      1 E. micrantha Reichb.
          E. gracilis (Fr.) Drej.
          E. micrantha × scottica = E. × electa Townsend
          E. micrantha × nemorosa
      2 E. scottica Wettst.
      3 E. rhumica Pugsl.
      4 E. frigida Pugsl.
          E. arctica auct.; *E. latifolia* auct.
          E. frigida × micrantha
          E. frigida × scottica
      5 E. foulaensis Townsend ex Wettst.
          E. foulaensis × micrantha
          E. foulaensis × occidentalis
      6 E. eurycarpa Pugsl.
      7 E. campbelliae Pugsl.
      8 E. rotundifolia Pugsl.

9   E. marshallii Pugsl.
    E. marshallii × micrantha
    E. marshallii × rotundifolia
10 E. curta (Fr.) Wettst.
    E. curta × micrantha = E. × areschougii Wettst.
    E. curta × nemorosa
11 E. cambrica Pugsl.
12 E. occidentalis Wettst.
13 E. nemorosa (Pers.) Wallr.
        E. stricta auct.
    E. nemorosa × pseudokerneri
14 E. heslop-harrisonii Pugsl.
15 E. confusa Pugsl.
        E. atroviolacea Druce & Lumb; *E. lumbii* Druce;
            E. minima auct.
    E. confusa × frigida
    E. confusa × occidentalis
    E. confusa × nemorosa
    E. confusa × rostkoviana
16 E. pseudokerneri Pugsl.
        E. kerneri auct.; *E. stricta* auct.
17 E. borealis Wettst.
    E. borealis × micrantha
        E. caerulea auct.
    E. borealis × foulaensis
    E. borealis × marshallii
    E. borealis × brevipila
18 E. brevipila Burnat & Gremli
        E. notata Townsend; *E. suecica* auct.
    E. brevipila × micrantha = E. × difformis Townsend
    E. brevipila × scottica = E. × venusta Townsend
    E. brevipila × foulaensis
    E. brevipila × rotundifolia
    E. brevipila × marshallii
    E. brevipila × curta = E. × murbeckii Wettst.
        E. septentrionalis Druce & Lumb
    E. brevipila × occidentalis = E. × pratiuscula   Town-
        send
    E. brevipila × nemorosa
        E. campestris auct.
    E. brevipila × confusa
19 E. rostkoviana Hayne
20 E. montana Jord.
21 E. rivularis Pugsl.
22 E. anglica Pugsl.
        E. fennica auct.
    E. anglica × micrantha

99

    E. anglica × nemorosa = E. × glanduligera Wettst.
    E. rechingeri auct.
    E. anglica × confusa
    E. anglica × brevipila
    E. anglica × rostkoviana
23 E. vigursii Davey
24 E. hirtella Jord. ex Reut.

    E. officinalis × salisburgensis
2 E. salisburgensis Funck

436 **ODONTITES** Ludw.
    1 **O. verna (Bellardi) Dumort.**
     a subsp. verna
     b subsp. serotina (Wettst.) E. F. Warb.
         Bartsia odontites (L.) Huds.; *Odontites rubra*
         Gilib.; *O. vulgaris* Moench

437 **PARENTUCELLIA** Viv.
    Eufragia Griseb.

    1 **P. viscosa (L.) Caruel**
         Bartsia viscosa L.; *Lasiopera viscosa* (L.) Hoffmanns.
         & Link; *Eufragia viscosa* (L.) Benth.

438 **BARTSIA** L.
    1 **B. alpina L.**

OROBANCHACEAE

439 **LATHRAEA** L.
    1 **L. squamaria L.**
    2 *L. clandestina L.

440 **OROBANCHE** L.
    1 *O. ramosa L.
    2 **O. purpurea Jacq.**
         O. caerulea Vill.; *O. arenaria* auct.
    3 **O. rapum-genistae Thuill.**
         O. major auct.
    4 **O. alba Steph. ex Willd.**
         O. rubra Sm.
    5 **O. caryophyllacea Sm.**
         O. vulgaris Poir.

6   O. elatior Sutton
    O. major auct.
7   O. reticulata Wallr.
8   O. minor Sm.
    O. apiculata Wallr.; *O. ritro* auct.
9   O. picridis F. W. Schultz ex Koch
10 O. hederae Duby
11 O. maritima Pugsl.
    O. amethystea auct.

LENTIBULARIACEAE

441 PINGUICULA L.

1   P. lusitanica L.
2   †P. alpina L.
3   P. vulgaris L.
4   P. grandiflora Lam.
    P. grandiflora × vulgaris = P. × scullyi Druce

442 UTRICULARIA L.

1   U. vulgaris L.
2   U. neglecta Lehm.
    U. major auct.
3   U. intermedia Hayne
    U. ochroleuca auct.
4   U. minor L.
    U. bremii auct.

*ACANTHACEAE

443 *ACANTHUS L.

1   *A. mollis L.

VERBENACEAE

444 VERBENA L.

1   V. officinalis L.

LABIATAE

445 MENTHA L.

1   *M. requienii Benth.
2   M. pulegium L.

3 M. arvensis L.
   M. arvensis × spicata=M. × gentilis L.
     M. gracilis Sole; *M. cardiaca* (Gray) Bak.
   M. arvensis × rotundifolia=M. × muellerana   F. W.
     Schultz
4 M. aquatica L.
   M. aquatica × arvensis=M. × verticillata L.
     M. sativa L.
   M. aquatica × arvensis × spicata=M. × smithiana   R.
     A. Grah.
     M. rubra Sm., non Mill.
   M. aquatica × spicata=M. × piperita L.
     M. crispa L.; *M. citrata* Ehrh.; *M. hircina* Hull;
     M. fraseri Druce
   M. aquatica × longifolia=M. × dumetorum Schult.
     M. palustris Sole, non Mill.; *M. pubescens* auct.
   M. aquatica × rotundifolia=M. × maximilianea F. W.
     Schultz
5 *M. spicata L.
     M. viridis auct.; *M. villosonervata* auct.
6 M. longifolia (L.) Huds.
     M. sylvestris L.; *M. nouletiana* auct.
   M. longifolia × rotundifolia=M. × niliaca   Juss.   ex
     Jacq.
     M. alopecuroides Hull
7 M. rotundifolia (L.) Huds.
   *M. rotundifolia × spicata=M. × cordifolia Opiz

446 LYCOPUS L.
   1 L. europaeus L.

447 ORIGANUM L.
   1 O. vulgare L.

448 THYMUS L.
   1 T. pulegioides L.
     T. glaber Mill.; *T. ovatus* Mill; *T. chamaedrys* Fr.
   2 T. serpyllum L.
   3 T. drucei Ronn.
     T. neglectus Ronn.; *T. britannicus* Ronn.; *T. zetlandicus* Ronn. & Druce; *T. pseudolanuginosus* Ronn.; *T. serpyllum* auct.; *T. pycnotrichus* auct.; *T. lanuginosus* auct.; *T. carniolicus* auct.

449 *HYSSOPUS L.
 1 *H. officinalis L.

450 *SATUREJA L.
 1 *S. montana L.

451 CALAMINTHA Mill.
 1 C. sylvatica Bromf.
   Satureja sylvatica (Bromf.) Maly; *Calamintha intermedia* auct.; *Clinopodium grandiflorum* auct.
 2 C. ascendens Jord.
   Satureja ascendens (Jord.) Maly; *S. villosa* auct.; *Calamintha officinalis* auct.; *C. baetica* auct.; *Clinopodium calamintha* auct.
 3 C. nepeta (L.) Savi
   Satureja nepeta (L.) Scheele; *Clinopodium nepeta* (L.) Kuntze

452 ACINOS Mill.
 1 A. arvensis (Lam.) Dandy
   Calamintha acinos (L.) Clairv.; *Satureja acinos* (L.) Scheele; *Clinopodium acinos* (L.) Kuntze

453 CLINOPODIUM L.
 1 C. vulgare L.
   Calamintha clinopodium Benth.; *C. vulgaris* (L.) Druce, non Clairv.

454 *MELISSA L.
 1 *M. officinalis L.

455 SALVIA L.
 1 *S. verticillata L.
 2 S. pratensis L.
 3 *S. sylvestris L.
 4 S. horminoides Pourr.
   S. verbenaca auct.
 5 [S. verbenaca L.
   S. marquandii Druce; *S. clandestina* auct.]

456 MELITTIS L.
 1 M. melissophyllum L.

457 PRUNELLA L.
    1 P. vulgaris L.
    2 *P. laciniata (L.) L.
        P. laciniata × vulgaris = P. × intermedia Link
        P. hybrida Knaf

458 BETONICA L.
    1 B. officinalis L.
        Stachys betonica Benth.; *S. officinalis* (L.) Trev.

459 STACHYS L.
    1 *S. annua (L.) L.
    2 *S. recta L.
    3 S. arvensis (L.) L.
    4 S. germanica L.
    5 S. alpina L.
    6 S. palustris L.
        S. palustris × sylvatica = S. × ambigua Sm.
    7 S. sylvatica L.

460 BALLOTA L.
    1 B. nigra L.
      a *subsp. nigra
          B. ruderalis Sw.
      b subsp. foetida Hayek

461 GALEOBDOLON Adans.
    1 G. luteum Huds.
        Lamium galeobdolon (L.) L.

462 LAMIUM L.
    1 L. amplexicaule L.
    2 L. moluccellifolium Fr.
        L. intermedium Fr.
    3 L. hybridum Vill.
    4 L. purpureum L.
        L. boreale Druce
    5 L. album L.
    6 *L. maculatum L.

463 *LEONURUS L.
    1 *L. cardiaca L.

LABIATAE

464 *PHLOMIS L.
    1 *P. fruticosa L.
    2 *P. samia L.

465 GALEOPSIS L.
    1 G. angustifolia Ehrh. ex Hoffm.
        G. ladanum auct.
    2 *G. ladanum L.
        G. intermedia Vill.
    3 G. segetum Neck.
        G. dubia Leers
    4 G. tetrahit L. *sensu lato*

        1 G. tetrahit L.
        2 G. bifida Boenn.
            G. sulfurea Druce
    5 G. speciosa Mill.

466 NEPETA L.
    1 N. cataria L.

467 GLECHOMA L.
    1 G. hederacea L.
        Nepeta glechoma Benth.; *N. hederacea* (L.) Trev.

468 MARRUBIUM L.
    1 M. vulgare L.

469 SCUTELLARIA L.
    1 S. galericulata L.
        S. galericulata × minor = S. × hybrida Strail
        S. nicholsoni Taub.
    2 S. minor Huds.
    3 *S. hastifolia L.
    4 *S. altissima L.
        S. columnae auct.

470 TEUCRIUM L.
    1 *T. chamaedrys L.
    2 T. scordium L.
    3 T. botrys L.
    4 T. scorodonia L.

471 AJUGA L.

    1 A. chamaepitys (L.) Schreb.
    2 A. reptans L.
    3 *A. genevensis L.
    4 A. pyramidalis L.
       A. pyramidalis × reptans = A. × hampeana Braun & Vatke
       A. hybrida Druce, non A. Kerner

PLANTAGINACEAE

472 PLANTAGO L.

    1 P. major L.
    2 P. media L.
    3 P. lanceolata L.
       P. timbali Jord.
    4 P. maritima L.
       P. hudsoniana Druce; *P. edmondstonii* Druce
    5 P. coronopus L.
       P. sabrinae (Cardew & Bak.) Druce
    6 *P. indica L.
       P. psyllium L., *nom. ambig.*; *P. arenaria* Waldst. & Kit.; *P. ramosa* Aschers.
    7 *P. sempervirens Crantz
       P. cynops L. 1762, non L. 1753

473 LITTORELLA Berg.

    1 L. uniflora (L.) Aschers.
       L. lacustris L.

CAMPANULACEAE

474 WAHLENBERGIA Schrad.
    Cervicina Del.

    1 W. hederacea (L.) Reichb.
       Campanula hederacea L.; *Cervicina hederacea* (L.) Druce

475 CAMPANULA L.

    1 C. latifolia L.
    2 C. trachelium L.
    3 *C. rapunculoides L.

4 *C. lactiflora Bieb.
5 *C. persicifolia L.
6 C. glomerata L.
7 C. rotundifolia L.
8 C. patula L.
9 *C. rapunculus L.
10 *C. alliariifolia Willd.
11 *C. medium L.

476 **LEGOUSIA** Durande
  Specularia A. DC.
  1 L. hybrida (L.) Delarb.
    Campanula hybrida L.; *Specularia hybrida* (L.) A. DC.

477 ***TRACHELIUM L.**
  1 *T. caeruleum L.

478 **PHYTEUMA L.**
  1 P. tenerum R. Schulz
    P. orbiculare auct.
  2 P. spicatum L.

479 **JASIONE L.**
  1 J. montana L.

480 **LOBELIA L.**
  1 L. urens L.
  2 · L. dortmanna L.

RUBIACEAE

481 **SHERARDIA L.**
  1 S. arvensis L.

482 ***PHUOPSIS** (Griseb.) Hook. f.
  1 *P. stylosa (Trin.) B. D. Jackson
    Asperula ciliata auct.

483 ASPERULA L.
 1 *A. taurina L.
 2 A. cynanchica L.

484 CRUCIATA Mill.
 1 C. chersonensis (Willd.) Ehrend.
   Galium cruciata (L.) Scop.

485 GALIUM L.
 1 G. odoratum (L.) Scop.
   Asperula odorata L.
 2 G. boreale L.
 3 G. mollugo L.
  a subsp. mollugo
  b subsp. erectum Syme
    G. erectum Huds. 1778 *pro parte*
  G. mollugo × verum = G. × pomeranicum Retz.
   G. ochroleucum Wolf ex Schweigg. & Koerte; *G.*
   hillardiae Druce
 4 G. verum L.
 5 G. saxatile L.
   G. harcynicum Weigel
 6 G. pumilum Murr.
   G. sylvestre Poll., non Scop.; *G. umbellatum* Lam.
 7 G. sterneri Ehrend.
 8 G. palustre L.
  a subsp. palustre
    G. witheringii Sm.
  b subsp. elongatum (C. Presl) Lange
    G. elongatum C. Presl
 9 G. debile Desv.
   G. constrictum Chaub.
 10 G. uliginosum L.
 11 G. tricornutum Dandy
   G. tricorne Stokes *pro parte*
 12 G. aparine L.
 13 G. spurium L.
   G. vaillantii DC.
 14 G. parisiense L.
   G. anglicum Huds.

486 RUBIA L.
 1 R. peregrina L.

CAPRIFOLIACEAE

487 SAMBUCUS L.
1   S. ebulus L.
2   S. nigra L.
3 *S. racemosa L.

488 VIBURNUM L.
1   V. lantana L.
2 *V. tinus L.
3   V. opulus L.

489 *SYMPHORICARPOS Duham.
1 *S. rivularis Suksd.
      S. albus auct.; *S. racemosus* auct.; *S. symphoricarpos*
      auct.

490 LINNAEA L.
1   L. borealis L.

491 LONICERA L.
1   L. xylosteum L.
2 *L. japonica Thunb.
3   L. periclymenum L.
4 *L. caprifolium L.

492 *LEYCESTERIA Wall.
1 *L. formosa Wall.

ADOXACEAE

493 ADOXA L.
1   A. moschatellina L.

VALERIANACEAE

494 VALERIANELLA Mill.
1   V. locusta (L.) Betcke
      V. olitoria (L.) Poll.
2   V. carinata Lois.
3   V. rimosa Bast.
      V. auricula DC.
4 *V. eriocarpa Desv.
5   V. dentata (L.) Poll.

495 VALERIANA L.
  1 V. officinalis L.
     V. sambucifolia Mikan f.
  2 *V. pyrenaica L.
  3 V. dioica L.

496 *CENTRANTHUS DC.
  1 *C. ruber (L.) DC.

<h2 style="text-align:center">DIPSACACEAE</h2>

497 DIPSACUS L.
  1 D. fullonum L.
     D. sylvestris Huds.
  2 D. pilosus L.

498 KNAUTIA L.
  1 K. arvensis (L.) Coult.
     Scabiosa arvensis L.

499 SCABIOSA L.
  1 S. columbaria L.
  2 *S. atropurpurea L.
     S. maritima L.

500 SUCCISA Haller
  1 S. pratensis Moench
     Scabiosa succisa L.

<h2 style="text-align:center">COMPOSITAE</h2>

501 *RUDBECKIA L.
  1 *R. laciniata L.

502 BIDENS L.
  1 B. cernua L.
  2 B. tripartita L.
     B. peacockii Druce
  3 *B. frondosa L.

503 *GALINSOGA Ruiz & Pav.
  1 *G. parviflora Cav.
  2 *G. ciliata (Raf.) Blake
     G. quadriradiata auct.

504 *AMBROSIA L.

> 1 *A. artemisiifolia L.
> *A. elatior* L.

505 *XANTHIUM L.

> 1 *X. strumarium L.
> 2 *X. spinosum L.

506 SENECIO L.

> 1 S. jacobaea L.
> 2 S. aquaticus Hill
> > *S. erraticus* auct.
> > S. aquaticus × jacobaea = S. × ostenfeldii Druce
> 3 S. erucifolius L.
> 4 *S. squalidus L.
> > S. squalidus × viscosus = S. × londinensis Lousley
> > S. squalidus × vulgaris
> 5 S. cambrensis Rosser
> 6 S. sylvaticus L.
> > S. sylvaticus × viscosus = S. × viscidulus Scheele
> 7 S. viscosus L.
> 8 S. vulgaris L.
> > *S. lanuginosus* Trow, non Spreng.
> 9 *S. tanguticus Maxim.
> 10 *S. smithii DC.
> 11 †S. paludosus L.
> 12 *S. doria L.
> 13 *S. fluviatilis Wallr.
> > *S. sarracenicus* auct.
> 14 *S. inaequidens DC.
> > *S. lautus* auct.
> 15 *S. mikanioides Otto ex Walp.
> 16 †S. palustris (L.) Hook.
> > *S. congestus* (R. Br.) DC.
> 17 S. integrifolius (L.) Clairv. *sensu lato*
> > > *1* S. integrifolius (L.) Clairv.
> > > > *S. campestris* (Retz.) DC.
> > > *2* S. spathulifolius Turcz.
> 18 *S. cineraria DC.
> > S. cineraria × jacobaea = S. × albescens Burbidge &
> > Colgan

COMPOSITAE

507 *DORONICUM L.
 1 *D. pardalianches L.
 2 *D. plantagineum L.

508 TUSSILAGO L.
 1 T. farfara L.

509 PETASITES Mill.
 1 P. hybridus (L.) Gaertn., Mey. & Scherb.
   Tussilago petasites L.; *Petasites ovatus* Hill; *P. vulgaris* Desf.; *P. petasites* (L.) Karst.
 2 *P. albus (L.) Gaertn.
 3 *P. japonicus (Sieb. & Zucc.) F. Schmidt
 4 *P. fragrans (Vill.) C. Presl
   Tussilago fragrans Vill.

510 *HOMOGYNE Cass.
 1 *H. alpina (L.) Cass.
   Tussilago alpina L.

511 *CALENDULA L.
 1 *C. officinalis L.
 2 *C. arvensis L.

512 INULA L.
 1 *I. helenium L.
 2 I. salicina L.
 3†*I. britannica L.
 4 I. conyza DC.
   I. squarrosa (L.) Bernh., non L.; *I. vulgaris* Trev.
 5 I. crithmoides L.
 6 *I. viscosa (L.) Ait.
 7 *I. graveolens (L.) Desf.

513 PULICARIA Gaertn.
 1 P. dysenterica (L.) Bernh.
   Inula dysenterica L.
 2 P. vulgaris Gaertn.
   Inula pulicaria L.; *Pulicaria prostrata* Aschers.; *P. pulicaria* (L.) Karst.

112

514 FILAGO L.
  1 F. germanica (L.) L.
  2 F. apiculata G. E. Sm.
  3 F. spathulata C. Presl
  4 *F. gallica L.
  5 F. minima (Sm.) Pers.

515 GNAPHALIUM L.
  1 G. sylvaticum L.
  2 G. norvegicum Gunn.
  3 G. supinum L.
  4 G. uliginosum L.
  5 G. luteoalbum L.
  6 [*G. undulatum L.]

516 *ANAPHALIS DC.
  1 *A. margaritacea (L.) Benth.
      Antennaria margaritacea (L.) Gray

517 ANTENNARIA Gaertn.
  1 A. dioica (L.) Gaertn.
      A. hyperborea D. Don; *A. hibernica* Braun-Blanq.

518 SOLIDAGO L.
  1 S. virgaurea L.
      S. cambrica Huds.; *S. angustifolia* Mill.
  2 *S. canadensis L.
  3 *S. gigantea Ait.
      S. serotina Ait., non Retz.
  4 *S. graminifolia (L.) Salisb.
      S. lanceolata L.

519 ASTER L.
  1 A. tripolium L.
  2 *A. macrophyllus L.
  3 *A. novae-angliae L.
  4 *A. puniceus L.
  5 *A. longifolius Lam.
  6 *A. novi-belgii L.
      a *subsp. novi-belgii
      b *subsp. floribundus (Willd.) Thell.
      c *subsp. laevigatus (Lam.) Thell.
          A. laevigatus Lam.

7 *A. laevis L.
   *A. laevis × novi-belgii = A. × versicolor Willd.
8 *A. lanceolatus Willd.
      A. paniculatus auct.; *A. lamarckianus* auct.
9 *A. salignus Willd.

520 CRINITARIA Cass.
   Linosyris Cass., non Ludw.
   1 C. linosyris (L.) Less.
      Aster linosyris (L.) Bernh.; *Linosyris vulgaris* Less.
      ex DC.

521 ERIGERON L.
   1 E. acer L.
   2 E. borealis (Vierh.) Simmons
      E. alpinus auct.
   3 ‡E. uniflorus L.
   4 *E. glaucus Ker-Gawl.
   5 *E. mucronatus DC.
      E. karvinskianus var. *mucronatus* (DC.) Aschers.

522 *CONYZA Less.
   1 *C. canadensis (L.) Cronq.
      Erigeron canadensis L.

CONYZA × ERIGERON
   C. canadensis × E. acer
   Erigeron huelsenii Vatke

523 *OLEARIA Moench
   1 *O. macrodonta Bak.

524 BELLIS L.
   1 B. perennis L.

525 EUPATORIUM L.
   1 E. cannabinum L.

526 ANTHEMIS L.
   1 *A. tinctoria L.
   2 A. cotula L.
   3 A. arvensis L.
      A. anglica Spreng.

COMPOSITAE

527 CHAMAEMELUM Mill.
  1 C. nobile (L.) All.
     Anthemis nobilis L.

528 ACHILLEA L.
  1 A. millefolium L.
  2 *A. tomentosa L.
  3 A. ptarmica L.

529 OTANTHUS Hoffmanns. & Link
    Diotis Desf., non Schreb.
  1 O. maritimus (L.) Hoffmanns. & Link
     Diotis maritima (L.) Desf. ex Cass.

530 *SANTOLINA L.
  1 *S. chamaecyparissus L.

531 TRIPLEUROSPERMUM Schultz Bip.
  1 T. maritimum (L.) Koch
     Matricaria maritima L.
  a subsp. maritimum
  b subsp. inodorum (L.) Hyland. ex Vaarama
     Matricaria inodora L.; *M. maritima* subsp.
     indora (L.) Clapham

532 MATRICARIA L.
  1 M. recutita L.
     M. chamomilla auct.
  2 *M. matricarioides (Less.) Porter
     M. discoidea DC.; *M. suaveolens* (Pursh) Buchen.,
     non L.; *M. occidentalis* Greene

533 CHRYSANTHEMUM L.
    Tanacetum L.
  1 C. segetum L.
  2 C. leucanthemum L.
  3 *C. maximum Ramond
  4 *C. parthenium (L.) Bernh.
     Matricaria parthenium L.
  5 C. vulgare (L.) Bernh.
     Tanacetum vulgare L.

115

COMPOSITAE

534 *COTULA L.
   1 *C. coronopifolia L.

535 ARTEMISIA L.
   1 A. vulgaris L.
   2 *A. verlotorum Lamotte
   3 *A. biennis Willd.
   4 *A. stellerana Bess.
   5 A. norvegica Fr.
   6 A. absinthium L.
   7 A. maritima L.
   8 A. campestris L.

536 *ECHINOPS L.
   1 *E. sphaerocephalus L.

537 CARLINA L.
   1 C. vulgaris L.

538 ARCTIUM L.
   1 A. lappa L.
       A. *majus* Bernh.
       A. lappa × pubens=A. × debrayi Senay
       A. lappa × minus=A. × nothum (Ruhmer) J. Weiss
   2 A. nemorosum Lejeune
       A. *intermedium* Lange; *A. vulgare* auct.
   3 A. pubens Bab.
       A. *vulgare* auct.
   4 A. minus Bernh.

539 CARDUUS L.
   1 C. tenuiflorus Curt.
       C. *pycnocephalus* auct.
   2 *C. pycnocephalus L.
   3 C. nutans L.
   4 C. acanthoides L.
       C. *crispus* auct.
       C. acanthoides × nutans=C. × orthocephalus Wallr.

540 CIRSIUM Mill.
   1 C. eriophorum (L.) Scop.
       Carduus eriophorus L.; *Cnicus eriophorus* (L.) Roth
       C. eriophorum × vulgare=C. × gerhardtii Schultz Bip.

116

2   C. vulgare (Savi) Ten.
Carduus lanceolatus L.; *Cirsium lanceolatum* (L.) Scop., non Hill; *Cnicus lanceolatus* (L.) Willd.

3   C. palustre (L.) Scop.
Carduus palustris L.; *Cnicus palustris* (L.) Willd.
C. palustre × vulgare = C. × subspinuligerum Peterm.
C. palustre × tuberosum = C. × semidecurrens Richt.

4   C. arvense (L.) Scop.
Carduus arvensis (L.) Hill; *Cnicus arvensis* (L.) Roth
C. arvense × vulgare = C. × csepeliense Borbás
C. arvense × palustre = C. × celakovskianum Knaf

5   *C. oleraceum (L.) Scop.
Cnicus oleraceus L.

6   C. acaulon (L.) Scop.
Carduus acaulos L.; *Cnicus acaulos* (L.) Willd.
C. acaulon × vulgare = C. × sabaudum Löhr
C. acaulon × arvense = C. × boulayi Camus
C. acaulon × dissectum = C. × woodwardii (H. C. Wats.) Nyman
Carduus woodwardii H. C. Wats.; *Cnicus woodwardii* (H. C. Wats.) Hook. f.
C. acaulon × tuberosum = C. × zizianum Koch

7   C. heterophyllum (L.) Hill
Carduus heterophyllus L.; *Cnicus heterophyllus* (L.) Roth
C. heterophyllum × vulgare = C. × breunium Goller & Huter
C. heterophyllum × palustre = C. × wankelii Reichardt
Carduus carolorum Howie & Jenner; *Cnicus carolorum* (Howie & Jenner) Hook. f.; *C. wankelii* (Reichardt) F. J. Hanb.

8   C. dissectum (L.) Hill
Carduus pratensis Huds.; *Cnicus pratensis* (Huds.) Willd.; *Cirsium anglicum* (Lam.) DC.; *C. pratense* (Huds.) Druce, non DC.
C. dissectum × palustre = C. × forsteri (Sm.) Loud.
Cnicus forsteri Sm.; *Carduus forsteri* (Sm.) Bab.
C. dissectum × tuberosum

9   C. tuberosum (L.) All.
Carduus tuberosus L.; *Cnicus tuberosus* (L.) Roth

541 *SILYBUM Adans.
    Mariana Hill
    1 *S. marianum (L.) Gaertn.
        Carduus marianus L.; *Mariana mariana* (L.) Hill

542 ONOPORDUM L.
    1 O. acanthium L.

543 SAUSSUREA DC.
    1 S. alpina (L.) DC.

544 CENTAUREA L.
    1 C. scabiosa L.
    2 *C. montana L.
    3 C. cyanus L.
    4 [*C. paniculata L.]
    5 *C. jacea L.
        C. angustifolia auct.
        C. jacea × nigra = C. × drucei C. E. Britton
        C. pratensis auct.; *C. jungens* auct.
        C. jacea × nemoralis = C. × moncktonii C. E. Britton
        C. surrejana C. E. Britton; ? *C. nemophila* auct.;
          ? *C. viretorum* auct.; ? *C. subjacea* auct.
    6 C. nigra L.
        C. obscura Jord.
    7 C. nemoralis Jord.
        C. nigra subsp. *nemoralis* (Jord.) Gugler
        C. nemoralis × nigra
    8 C. aspera L.
    9 *C. calcitrapa L.
  10 *C. solstitialis L.

545 SERRATULA L.
    1 S. tinctoria L.

546 CICHORIUM L.
    1 C. intybus L.

547 LAPSANA L.
    1 L. communis L.
    2 *L. intermedia Bieb.

548 ARNOSERIS Gaertn.
    1 A. minima (L.) Schweigg. & Koerte
       A. pusilla Gaertn.

549 HYPOCHOERIS L.
    1 H. radicata L.
    2 H. glabra L.
       H. glabra × radicata
    3 H. maculata L.

550 LEONTODON L.
    Thrincia Roth
    1 L. autumnalis L.
    2 L. hispidus L.
    3 L. taraxacoides (Vill.) Mérat
       Thrincia hirta Roth; *T. leysseri* Wallr.; *T. taraxa-coides* (Vill.) Gaudin; *Leontodon leysseri* G. Beck; *Thrincia nudicaulis* Britten *pro parte*; *Leontodon hirtus* auct.; *L. nudicaulis* auct.

551 PICRIS L.
    Helmintia Juss.
    1 P. echioides L.
       Helmintia echioides (L.) Gaertn.
    2 P. hieracioides L.
       P. spinulosa auct.

552 TRAGOPOGON L.
    1 T. pratensis L.
      a subsp. pratensis
      b subsp. minor (Mill.) Wahlenb.
         T. minor Mill.
    2 *T. porrifolius L.
       T. porrifolius × pratensis

553 SCORZONERA L.
    1 S. humilis L.

554 LACTUCA L.
    1 L. serriola L.
       L. scariola L.
    2 L. virosa L.
    3 L. saligna L.
    4 *L. tatarica (L.) C. A. Mey.

COMPOSITAE

555 MYCELIS Cass.

  1 M. muralis (L.) Dumort.
     Lactuca muralis (L.) Gaertn.

556 SONCHUS L.

  1 S. palustris L.
  2 S. arvensis L.
  3 S. oleraceus L.
     S. piquetii Druce
  4 S. asper (L.) Hill
     S. asper × oleraceus

557 CICERBITA Wallr.

  1 C. alpina (L.) Wallr.
     Mulgedium alpinum (L.) Less.; *Lactuca alpina* (L.)
     A. Gray
  2 *C. bourgaei (Boiss.) Beauverd
  3 *C. macrophylla (Willd.) Wallr.
     Lactuca macrophylla (Willd.) A. Gray

558 HIERACIUM L.[1]

  1 H. murorum L. *sensu lato*

  (*Sect. Amplexicaulia Fr.)

    1 *H. amplexicaule L.
    2 *H. pulmonarioides Vill.
    3 *H. speluncarum Arv.-Touv.

  (Sect. Alpina Fr.)

    4 H. alpinum L.
      H. nigrosetosum (Zahn) Roffey
    5 H. holosericeum Backh.
    6 H. grovesii Pugsl.
    7 H. eximium Backh.
      H. tenellum (Backh.) Druce
    8 H. calenduliflorum Backh.
    9 H. macrocarpum Pugsl.
   10 H. graniticola W. R. Linton
   11 H. gracilentum Backh.

[1] The arrangement in this genus is by Mr. P. D. Sell and Dr. C. West, who, with certain modifications, have followed that of H. W. Pugsley, *A Prodromus of the British Hieracia*, in Journ. Linn. Soc. Lond., Bot. 54: 1–356 (1948). For convenience sectional headings are inserted in parentheses, but it must be stressed that the "sections" are groupings of microspecies and do not correspond to sections as generally understood in other genera.

12 H. globosiflorum Pugsl.
    H. globosum Backh., non Desf.
13 H. pseudopetiolatum (Zahn) Roffey
    H. petiolatum auct.
14 H. backhousei F. J. Hanb.
15 H. pseudocurvatum (Zahn) Pugsl.
    H. curvatum auct.; *H. nigrescens* auct.
16 H. hanburyi Pugsl.
    H. chrysanthum Backh., non Ledeb.
17 H. subgracilentipes (Zahn) Roffey

(Sect. Subalpina Pugsl.)

18 H. lingulatum Backh.
19 H. molybdochroum (Dahlst.) Omang
20 H. marshallii E. F. Linton
21 H. cremnanthes (F. J. Hanb.) Pugsl.
22 H. pulmonarium Sm.
    H. sinuans F. J. Hanb.
23 H. senescens Backh.
24 H. pseudanglicum Pugsl.
25 H. gracilifolium (F. J. Hanb.) Pugsl.
    H. subnigrescens Norrlin, non Simonk.; *H. atratum* auct.
26 H. submurorum Lindeb.
    ? *H. gravastellum* auct.
27 H. cumbriense F. J. Hanb.
28 H. centripetale F. J. Hanb.
29 H. hyparcticoides Pugsl.
    H. hyparcticum auct.
30 H. isabellae E. S. Marshall
31 H. callistophyllum F. J. Hanb.
32 H. dasythrix (E. F. Linton) Pugsl.

(Sect. Cerinthoidea Fr.)

33 H. anglicum Fr.
    H. subimpressum Dahlst.; *H. patens* Dahlst.; *H. cerinthoides* auct.
34 H. hartii (F. J. Hanb.) Sell & West
    H. anglicum var. *hartii* (F. J. Hanb.) F. N. Williams
35 H. brigantum (F. J. Hanb.) Roffey
36 H. ebudicum Pugsl.
37 H. hebridense Pugsl.
38 H. ampliatum (W. R. Linton) A. Ley
    H. jaculifolium (F. J. Hanb.) Roffey
39 H. petrocharis (E. F. Linton) W. R. Linton
40 H. langwellense F. J. Hanb.

COMPOSITAE

41 H. flocculosum Backh.
42 H. shoolbredii E. S. Marshall
   H. skyense (Zahn) Roffey
43 H. iricum Fr.
44 H. scarpicum Pugsl.

(Sect. Oreadea Fr.)

45 H. lasiophyllum Koch
46 H. stenopholidium (Dahlst.) Omang
47 H. schmidtii Tausch
   H. lima F. J. Hanb.; *H. lasiophyllum* var. *euryodon*
      F. J. Hanb.; *H. crinigerum* Roffey *pro parte*;
      ? *H. dentifex* E. F. Linton
48 H. eustomon (E. F. Linton) Roffey
   H. devoniense (F. J. Hanb.) Roffey
49 H. leyi F. J. Hanb.
50 H. nitidum Backh.
   H. carenorum F. J. Hanb.
51 H. sommerfeltii Lindeb.
   H. basicrinum (Zahn) Roffey
52 H. carneddorum Pugsl.
53 H. argenteum Fr.
   H. oreades var. *subglabratum* F. J. Hanb.; *H.
      pseudomicrodon* Dahlst.; *H. orimeles* var.
      argentatum Pugsl.; *H. stenotum* auct.
54 H. vagense (F. J. Hanb.) A. Ley
55 H. cambricum (Bak.) F. J. Hanb.
56 H. subrude (Arv.-Touv.) Arv.-Touv.
   H. griffithii (F. J. Hanb.) F. J. Hanb.; *H. onos-
      moides* var. *buglossoides* F. J. Hanb. *pro parte*;
      H. deganwyense Pugsl.; *H. buglossoides* sensu
      Pugsl.
57 H. scoticum F. J. Hanb.
   H. pseudozetlandicum Roffey; *H. caledonicum* var.
      pseudozetlandicum (Roffey) Pugsl.
58 H. chloranthum Pugsl.
   H. pseudonosmoides auct.; *H. saxifragum* var.
      pseudonosmoides auct.
59 H. orimeles F. J. Hanb. ex W. R. Linton
   H. beebyanum Pugsl.

(Sect. Suboreadea Pugsl.)

60 H. repandulare Druce
   H. repandum A. Ley, non Schrank; *H. pseudo-
      repandum* Pugsl.
61 H. riddelsdellii Pugsl.
62 H. basalticola Pugsl.
   H. britannicum sensu Pugsl. *pro parte*

122

63 H. jovimontis (Zahn) Roffey
      H. superbum Roffey *pro parte*
64 H. cyathis (A. Ley) W. R. Linton
65 H. hypochoeroides Gibson
66 H. saxorum (F. J. Hanb.) Sell & West
      H. hypochoeroides var. *saxorum* F. J. Hanb.;
      H. sommerfeltii var. *subtruncatum* Pugsl.
67 H. subplanifolium Pugsl.
      H. devoniense Roffey *pro parte*
68 H. britannicum F. J. Hanb.
69 H. dicella Sell & West
      H. britannicum var. *ovale* A. Ley; *H. furcilliferum*
      Dahlst., non Omang; *H. britannicum* var.
      glaucinum Pugsl.; *H. britannicum* sensu Pugsl.
      pro parte
70 H. subbritannicum (A. Ley) Sell & West
      H. britannicum var. *subbritannicum* (A. Ley) Pugsl.
71 H. stenolepiforme (Pugsl.) Sell & West
      H. britannicum var. *stenolepiforme* Pugsl.; *H.
      caesium* auct.; *H. stenolepis* auct.
72 H. sarcophylloides Dahlst.
      H. expallidiforme Roffey *pro parte*; *H. dasypodum*
      Dahlst.
73 H. britanniciforme Pugsl.
74 H. clovense E. F. Linton
      H. leucograptum auct.
75 H. uistense (Pugsl.) Sell & West
      H. clovense var. *uistense* Pugsl.
76 H. fratrum Pugsl.
      H. sordidum W. R. Linton ex E. F. Linton, non
      Gillies

(Sect. Vulgata Fr.)
77 H. pachyphylloides (Zahn) Roffey
      H. pachyphyllum (Purchas) F. N. Williams, non
      Brenner
78 H. sanguineum (A. Ley) W. R. Linton
      H. subsanguineum (Zahn) Roffey
79 H. tricolorans (Zahn) Pugsl.
      H. expallidiforme Roffey *pro parte*; *H. cordigerum*
      var. *tricolorans* (Zahn) Roffey
80 H. subcyaneum (W. R. Linton) Pugsl.
      H. cordigerum var. *asymmetricum* (A. Ley) Roffey;
      H. cordigerum var. *subcyaneum* (W. R. Linton)
      Roffey
81 H. silvaticoides Pugsl.
82 H. maculosum (Stenstr.) Omang

123

83 H. pseudosarcophyllum Pugsl.
   H. sarcophyllum auct.
84 H. anguinum (W. R. Linton) Roffey
85 H. neocoracinum Pugsl.
86 H. prolixum Norrlin
87 H. subtenue (W. R. Linton) Roffey
88 H. aggregatum Backh.
89 H. oxyodus W. R. Linton
90 H. cillense Pugsl.
91 H. cymbifolium Purchas
92 H. scotostictum Hyland.
   H. praecox sensu Pugsl.
93 H. camptopetalum (F. J. Hanb.) Sell & West
   H. duriceps var. *camptopetalum* (F. J. Hanb.) Pugsl.
94 H. duriceps F. J. Hanb.
   H. pulcherrimum (F. J. Hanb.) Roffey; *H. killinense* (Zahn) Roffey; *H. micracladium* auct.
95 H. praetenerum Almq. ex Dahlst.
96 H. pellucidum Laest.
   H. lucidulum (A. Ley) Roffey
97 H. asteridiophyllum Sell & West
   H. pellucidum var. *lucidulum* W. R. Linton *pro parte* et sensu Pugsl.
98 H. exotericum Jord. ex Bor.
99 H. grandidens Dahlst.
   H. exotericum forma *grandidens* (Dahlst.) Pugsl.
100 H. cinderella (A. Ley) A. Ley
   H. exotericum var. *cinderella* (A. Ley) Pugsl.
101 H. candelabrae W. R. Linton
   H. exotericum var. *candelabrae* (W. R. Linton) Pugsl.
102 H. sublepistoides (Zahn) Druce
   H. lepistoides var. *sublepistoides* (Zahn) Roffey; *H. exotericum* var. *sublepistoides* (Zahn) Pugsl.; *H. integratum* auct.
103 H. glevense (Pugsl.) Sell & West
   H. sparsidens var. *elatius* (A. Ley) Roffey; *H. elatius* (A. Ley) Druce, non Rehm.; *H. stenstroemii* var. *subcordatum* Pugsl.; *H. exotericum* var. *glevense* Pugsl.; *H. cuneifrons* var. *decipiens* Pugsl.; *H. crassiceps* auct.; *H. torticeps* auct.; *H. subulatidens* auct.
104 H. cuneifrons (W. R. Linton) Pugsl.
105 H. snowdoniense Sell & West
   H. pulcherrimum sensu Pugsl.
106 H. itunense Pugsl.

107 H. pollinarium F. J. Hanb.
108 H. pictorum E. F. Linton
109 H. pollinarioides Pugsl.
110 H. caliginosum (Dahlst.) Roffey
111 H. subprasinifolium Pugsl.
112 H. pseudostenstroemii Pugsl.
   H. stenstroemii auct.
113 H. longilobum (Zahn) Roffey
114 H. semicrassiceps Pugsl.
   H. crassiceps auct.
115 H. ciliatiflorum Pugsl.
   H. ciliatum (Almq.) Dahlst., non Willd.
116 H. variicolor (Stenstr.) Omang
   H. orbicans auct.
117 H. dipteroides Dahlst.
118 H. oistophyllum Pugsl.
   H. sagittatum (Stenstr.) Dahlst., non Hoffmanns.
      & Link; *H. philanthrax* auct.; ? *H. orithales* E. F.
      Linton; ? *H. lintonianum* Druce
119 H. pycnodon (Dahlst.) Johans.
120 H. subhirtum (F. J. Hanb.) Pugsl.
121 H. rivale F. J. Hanb.
   H. morulum auct.
122 H. uisticola Pugsl.
123 H. breadalbanense F. J. Hanb.
124 H. crebridentiforme Pugsl.
   H. crebridens auct.
125 H. auratiflorum Pugsl.
126 H. lintonii A. Ley
   H. loennrothianum Roffey *pro parte*
127 H. euprepes F. J. Hanb.
   H. orcadense W. R. Linton; *H. holopleurum*
      Dahlst.; *H. subalpestrifrons* Dahlst.; *H. paraliae-*
      forme Dahlst.; *H. kalsoense* subsp. *burnense*
      Druce & Zahn; *H. subexpallescens* Dahlst.;
      H. clivicola (F. J. Hanb.) Pugsl.
128 H. angustatiforme Sell & West
   H. angustatum sensu Pugsl. *pro parte*
129 H. orarium Lindeb.
130 H. cacuminum (A. Ley) A. Ley
   H. nitidum var. *siluriense* F. J. Hanb.
131 H. rhomboides (Stenstr.) Johans.
   H. gravastellum var. *rhomboides* Stenstr.
132 H. melanochlorocephalum Pugsl.
133 H. stenophyes W. R. Linton
134 H. vennicontium Pugsl.
   H. duplicatum auct.

125

135 H. anfractiforme E. S. Marshall
  H. subanfractum E. S. Marshall; *H. neomarshallianum* (Zahn) Roffey
136 H. caesiomurorum Lindeb.
  H. dissimile sensu Pugsl.
137 H. subramosum Lönnr.
138 H. cravoniense (F. J. Hanb.) Roffey
139 H. rubiginosum F. J. Hanb.
  H. hypochoeroides var. *lancifolium* W. R. Linton; *H. caesiopilosum* Pugsl.
140 H. decolor (W. R. Linton) A. Ley
  H. smithii (Bak.) Druce; ? *H. pseudoleyi* (Zahn) Roffey
141 H. fulvocaesium Pugsl.
142 H. proximum F. J. Hanb.
  H. erythraeum E. F. Linton ex Pugsl.
143 H. caledonicum F. J. Hanb.
  H. farrense F. J. Hanb.; *H. rubicundum* F. J. Hanb.; *H. boswellii* E. F. Linton; *H. rubicundiforme* (Zahn) Roffey
144 H. angustisquamum (Pugsl.) Pugsl.
145 H. holophyllum W. R. Linton
146 H. leyanum (Zahn) Roffey
147 H. eustales E. F. Linton
148 H. insulare (F. J. Hanb.) F. J. Hanb.
149 H. vulgatum Fr.
  H. triviale Norrlin; *H. subravusculum* (W. R. Linton) Roffey; *H. subfasciculare* (W. R. Linton) Roffey; *H. sejunctum* (W. R. Linton) Roffey; *H. subconspersum* Roffey *pro parte*; *H. acroleucum* sensu Pugsl.
150 H. surrejanum F. J. Hanb.
151 H. subamplifolium (Zahn) Roffey
  H. megapodium Dahlst.
152 H. lepidulum (Stenstr.) Omang
153 H. roffeyanum Pugsl.
154 H. maculatum Sm.
155 H. submutabile (Zahn) Pugsl.
  H. mutabile (A. Ley) A. Ley, non F. W. Schultz; *H. argillaceum* var. *submutabile* (Zahn) Roffey; ? *H. reclinatum* auct.
156 H. rectulum A. Ley
157 H. diaphanoides Lindeb.
  H. diaphanoides var. *apiculatum* E. F. Linton; *H. praesigne* (Zahn) Roffey; *H. neopinnatifidum* Pugsl. *pro parte*; *H. megapodium* sensu Pugsl. *pro parte*; *H. subglaucovirens* auct.

158 H. diaphanum Fr.
      H. daedalolepioides (Zahn) Roffey
159 H. anglorum (A. Ley) Pugsl.
      H. megapodium Dahlst. *pro parte*; *H. diaphanoides*
      sensu Pugsl.; *H. ornatum* auct.; *H. scanicum*
      auct.; *H. irriguum* auct.; *H. cacuminatum* auct.;
      H. barbareifolium auct.; *H. scytophyllum* auct.;
      H. scotophyllum auct.
160 H. subminutidens (Zahn) Pugsl.
      H. adlerzii F. J. Hanb. *pro parte*
161 H. tunbridgense Pugsl.
162 H. cheriense Jord. ex Bor.
      H. lachenalii var. *pseudoporrigens* Pugsl.; *H.
      porrigens* auct.
163 H. strumosum (W. R. Linton) A. Ley
      H. chlorophyllum auct.
164 H. lachenalii C. C. Gmel.
      H. sciaphilum (Uechtr.) F. J. Hanb.; *H. deductum*
      Sudre; *H. jaccardii* Zahn
165 H. radyrense (Pugsl.) Sell & West
      H. lachenalii var. *radyrense* Pugsl.; *H. paucifolia-
      tum* auct.
166 H. acuminatum Jord.
167 H. pulchrius (A. Ley) W. R. Linton

(Sect. Alpestria Fr.)

168 H. dovrense Fr.
169 H. gratum Sell & West
      H. demissum var. *pulchelliforme* W. R. Linton;
      H. pulchelliforme (W. R. Linton) Pugsl., non
      Dahlst.; *H. pulchellum* auct.
170 H. zetlandicum Beeby
171 H. hethlandiae (F. J. Hanb.) Pugsl.
172 H. australius (Beeby) Pugsl.
      H. demissum var. *australius* (Beeby) Roffey;
      H. dovrense auct.
173 H. subtruncatum Beeby
      H. truncatum auct.
174 H. breve Beeby
175 H. praethulense Pugsl.
      ? *H. polycomatum* auct.
176 H. vinicaule Sell & West
      H. vinaceum (Beeby) Pugsl., non Johans. &
      Samuelss.; *H. platylepium* auct.
177 H. northroense Pugsl.
      H. congestum (Beeby) Roffey, non Freyn

127

COMPOSITAE

178 H. dewarii Syme
179 H. perthense F. N. Williams

(Sect. Prenanthoidea Koch)

180 H. prenanthoides Vill.
  H. strictissimum auct.; *H. subelatum* auct.; *H. lanceolatum* auct.
181 H. borreri Syme
  H. denticulatum sensu Pugsl.

(Sect. Tridentata Fr.)

182 H. hibernicum F. J. Hanb.
183 H. cambricogothicum Pugsl.
184 H. calviceps Pugsl.
  H. longiramosum Pugsl.
185 H. pseudacrifolium Pugsl.
  H. luescheri Roffey *pro parte*; *H. cambricogothicum* var. *glandulosum* Pugsl.; *H. fragilicaule* Pugsl.; *H. backhouseanum* var. *radnoricum* Pugsl.; *H. rhayaderense* Pugsl.; *H. obatrescens* auct.; *H. rigidum* auct.; ? *H. amphiboloides* (Zahn) Roffey
186 H. boreophilum (Zahn) Roffey
187 H. longiciliatum (F. J. Hanb.) Roffey
188 H. uiginskyense Pugsl.
  H. subgracilipes Roffey *pro parte*; *H. trinitatis* Pugsl.; *H. backhouseanum* sensu Pugsl. *pro parte*
189 H. gothicoides Pugsl.
  H. gothicum auct.; ? *H. backhouseanum* (Zahn) Roffey
190 H. scullyi W. R. Linton
191 H. stewartii (F. J. Hanb.) Roffey
  H. backhouseanum (Zahn) Roffey *pro parte*; *H. ardaricum* Pugsl.; *H. donegalense* Pugsl.; *H. hartianum* Pugsl.
192 H. substrigosum (Zahn) Roffey
193 H. placerophylloides Pugsl.
  H. grandescens sensu Pugsl. *pro parte*; *H. placerophyllum* auct.
194 H. oligodon (W. R. Linton) Pugsl.
  H. subintegrum Roffey *pro parte*
195 H. linguans (Zahn) Roffey
196 H. sparsifolium Lindeb.
  H. stictophyllum Dahlst. ex W. R. Linton; *H. pseudoprotractum* Pugsl., non Notø; *H. protractum* auct.
197 H. subintegrifolium Pugsl.

128

198 H. nidense (F. J. Hanb.) Roffey
199 H. scabrisetum (Zahn) Roffey
200 H. cantianum F. J. Hanb.
201 H. trichocaulon (Dahlst.) Johans.
    H. tridentatum sensu Pugsl. *pro parte*; *H. acrifolium*
    auct.; *H. scabrescens* auct.
202 H. acamptum Sell & West
    H. cantianum var. *subrigidum* W. R. Linton ex
    F. J. Hanb.
203 H. eboracense Pugsl.
    H. tridentatum sensu Pugsl. *pro parte*
204 H. calcaricola (F. J. Hanb.) Roffey
    H. tridentatum sensu Pugsl. *pro parte*; *H. scab-*
    rescens auct.
205 H. lissolepium (Zahn) Roffey

(Sect. Foliosa Fr.)
206 H. latobrigorum (Zahn) Roffey
    H. striatum var. *pseudauratum* Zahn; *H. pseud-*
    auratum (Zahn) Druce; *H. johnstonii* Dahlst.;
    H. polyphyllum Dahlst., non Willd.; *H. sub-*
    polyphyllum Pugsl.; *H. auratum* auct.
207 H. tavense (W. R. Linton) A. Ley
208 H. drummondii Pugsl.
209 H. subcrocatum (E. F. Linton) Roffey
    H. neocorymbosum Pugsl.; *H. bartonii* Pugsl.; *H.*
    corymbosum auct.; *H. salicifolium* auct.
210 H. strictiforme (Zahn) Roffey
    H. opsianthum (F. J. Hanb.) Roffey; *H. listerae*
    Pugsl.; *H. strictum* auct.
211 H. reticulatum Lindeb.
    H. pycnophyllum Roffey *pro parte*; *H. tridentati-*
    folium var. *melanoglochin* (E. F. Linton) Roffey
212 H. pseudamplidentatum Pugsl.
    H. tridentatifolium var. *amplidentatum* (F. J.
    Hanb.) Roffey; *H. subumbellatiforme* Roffey
    pro parte; *H. angustum* auct.
213 H. bakeranum Pugsl.
    H. crocatum auct.
214 H. pycnotrichum (W. R. Linton) Roffey
215 H. maritimum (F. J. Hanb.) F. J. Hanb.
216 H. obesifolium Pugsl.

(Sect. Umbellata Fr.)
217 H. umbellatum L.
    H. ogweni E. F. Linton
218 H. bichlorophyllum (Druce & Zahn) Pugsl.

(Sect. Sabauda Fr.)

219   H. perpropinquum (Zahn) Druce
> *H. sedunense* var. *perpropinquum* (Zahn) Roffey; *H. lugdunense* Roffey *pro parte*; *H. bladonii* Pugsl.; *H. argutifolium* Pugsl.; *H. eminentiforme* Pugsl.; *H. sabaudum* auct.; *H. boreale* auct.; *H. dumosum* auct.; *H. obliquum* auct.; *H. sedunense* auct.

220   H. virgultorum Jord.

221   H. rigens Jord.
> *H. nemorivagum* auct.

222   H. salticola (Sudre) Sell & West
> *H. sublactucaceum* sensu Pugsl. *pro parte*

223   H. vagum Jord.
> *H. sublactucaceum* Druce & Zahn *pro parte*; *H. calvatum* (F. J. Hanb.) Pugsl.; *H. croceostylum* Pugsl.; *H. subquercetorum* Pugsl.

2   H. pilosella L. *sensu lato*

(Sect. Pilosellina Fr.)

1   H. pilosella L.
> *H. tricholepium* (Naeg. & Peter) Roffey; *H. pernigrescens* (Zahn) Roffey; *H. pervirescens* (Zahn) Roffey; *H. subvirescens* Roffey *pro parte*; *H. latiusculum* (Naeg. & Peter) Roffey; *H. concinnatum* (F. J. Hanb.) Roffey; *H. vulgare* auct.

2   H. peleteranum Mérat

(*Sect. Auriculina Fr.)

3   *H. lactucella Wallr.
> *H. auricula* auct.

4   *H. helveolum (Dahlst.) Johans.

(*Sect. Collinina Naeg. & Peter)

5   *H. flagellare Willd.
> *H. stoloniflorum* auct.

6   *H. colliniforme (Naeg. & Peter) Roffey
> *H. pratense* auct.

7   *H. aurantiacum L.
> *H. claropurpureum* (Naeg. & Peter) Roffey

8   *H. brunneocroceum Pugsl.

(*Sect. Praealtina Naeg. & Peter)

9   *H. praealtum Vill. ex Gochnat

10   *H. arvorum (Naeg. & Peter) Pugsl.

11   *H. spraguei Pugsl.

559 CREPIS L.

1 C. foetida L.
2 *C. vesicaria L.
    *subsp. taraxacifolia (Thuill.) Thell.
       C. taraxacifolia Thuill.
3 *C. setosa Haller f.
4 C. mollis (Jacq.) Aschers.
    C. hieracioides Waldst. & Kit., non Lam.; *C. succisaefolia* (All.) Tausch
5 C. biennis L.
6 C. capillaris (L.) Wallr.
    C. virens L.
7 *C. nicaeensis Balb.
8 C. paludosa (L.) Moench

560 TARAXACUM Weber[1]

1 T. officinale Weber (Sect. Vulgaria: spp. 36–95 of *B.P.L.*)
    T. vulgare Schrank; *T. taraxacum* (L.) Karst.
2 T. palustre (Lyons) DC. (Sect. Palustria: spp. 14–15 of *B.P.L.*)
    T. paludosum (Scop.) Schlecht. ex Crép.; *T. balticum* Dahlst.
3 T. spectabile Dahlst. (Sect. Spectabilia: spp. 16–35 of *B.P.L.*)
4 T. laevigatum (Willd.) DC. (Sect. Erythrosperma + Sect. Obliqua: spp. 1–13 of *B.P.L.*)
    T. erythrospermum Andrz. ex Bess.; *T. obliquum* (Fr.) Dahlst.

MONOCOTYLEDONES

ALISMATACEAE

561 BALDELLIA Parl.

1 B. ranunculoides (L.) Parl.
    Alisma ranunculoides L.; *Echinodorus ranunculoides* (L.) Engelm.

---

[1] Four aggregate species of this genus are recognized here. Druce in the *British Plant List* (ed. 2), 72–73, enumerates 95 microspecies grouped in five sections. It is impracticable to list the names of all these microspecies in the synonymy given here; but references to them, by section and by number, are placed in parentheses after the names of the aggregate species.

562 LURONIUM Raf.
Elisma Buchen.
1 L. natans (L.) Raf.
Alisma natans L.; *Elisma natans* (L.) Buchen.

563 ALISMA L.
1 A. plantago-aquatica L.
A. gluckii Druce
2 A. lanceolatum With.
3 A. gramineum Lejeune

564 DAMASONIUM Mill.
1 D. alisma Mill.
D. stellatum Thuill.; *D. damasonium* (L.) Aschers. &
Graebn.

565 SAGITTARIA L.
1 S. sagittifolia L.
2 *S. latifolia Willd.
3 *S. rigida Pursh
S. heterophylla Pursh, non Schreb.

BUTOMACEAE

566 BUTOMUS L.
1 B. umbellatus L.

HYDROCHARITACEAE

567 HYDROCHARIS L.
1 H. morsus-ranae L.

568 STRATIOTES L.
1 S. aloides L.

569 *EGERIA Planch.
1 *E. densa Planch.

570 ELODEA Michx.
1 *E. canadensis Michx.
2 *E. callitrichoides (Rich.) Casp.
3 E. nuttallii (Planch.) St. John
Hydrilla lithuanica Dandy *pro parte*; *H. verticillata*
auct.

571 *LAGAROSIPHON Harv.

  1 *L. major (Ridl.) Moss

572 *VALLISNERIA L.

  1 *V. spiralis L.

SCHEUCHZERIACEAE

573 SCHEUCHZERIA L.

  1 S. palustris L.

JUNCAGINACEAE

574 TRIGLOCHIN L.

  1 T. palustris L.
  2 T. maritima L.

*APONOGETONACEAE

575 *APONOGETON L. f.

  1 *A. distachyos L. f.

ZOSTERACEAE

576 ZOSTERA L.

  1 Z. marina L.
  2 Z. angustifolia (Hornem.) Reichb.
    Z. hagstromii Druce; *Z. hornemanniana* Tutin
  3 Z. noltii Hornem.
    Z. nana auct.

POTAMOGETONACEAE

577 POTAMOGETON L.

  1 P. natans L.
    P. hibernicus (Hagstr.) Druce
  2 P. polygonifolius Pourr.
    P. oblongus Viv.; *P. spathulatus* auct.
  3 P. coloratus Hornem.
    P. plantagineus Du Croz ex Roem. & Schult.
    P. coloratus × gramineus = P. × billupsii Fryer
  4 P. nodosus Poir.
    P. drucei Fryer

5 P. lucens L.
    P. lucens × natans = P. × fluitans Roth
    P. crassifolius Fryer
    P. lucens × perfoliatus = P. × salicifolius Wolfg.
    P. decipiens Nolte ex Koch
6 P. gramineus L.
    P. heterophyllus Schreb.; *P. lonchites* Tuckerm.;
       P. varians Morong ex Fryer; *P. falcatus* Fryer;
       P. graminifolius H. & J. Groves; *P. seemenii* auct.
    P. gramineus × natans = P. × sparganifolius Laest. ex
       Fr.
    P. kirkii (Hook. f.) Syme ex Hook. f.
    P. gramineus × lucens = P. × zizii Koch ex Roth
    P. coriaceus (Mert. & Koch) A. Benn.; *P. babing-*
       tonii A. Benn.; *P. angustifolius* auct.; *P. longifolius*
       auct.
    P. gramineus × perfoliatus = P. × nitens Weber
    P. involutus (Fryer) H. & J. Groves
7 P. alpinus Balb.
    P. rufescens Schrad.
    P. alpinus × lucens = P. × nerviger Wolfg.
    P. alpinus × gramineus = P. × nericius Hagstr.
    P. alpinus × praelongus = P. × griffithii A. Benn.
    P. macvicarii A. Benn.
    P. alpinus × perfoliatus = P. × prussicus Hagstr.
    P. alpinus × crispus = P. × olivaceus Baagöe ex G.
       Fisch.
    P. venustus Baagöe ex A. Benn.
8 P. praelongus Wulf.
    P. undulatus auct.
9 P. perfoliatus L.
    P. perfoliatus × praelongus = P. × cognatus Aschers. &
       Graebn.
10 P. epihydrus Raf.
    P. pensylvanicus Willd. ex Cham. & Schlecht.
11 P. friesii Rupr.
    P. mucronatus Schrad. ex Sond.
12 P. rutilus Wolfg.
13 P. pusillus L.
    P. panormitanus Biv.; *P. rutilus* auct.; *P. dualis* auct.;
       P. franconicus auct.; *P. pusilliformis* auct.; *P.*
       sudermanicus auct.
    P. pusillus × trichoides = P. × trinervius G. Fisch.

14 P. obtusifolius Mert. & Koch
    P. sturrockii (A. Benn.) A. Benn.; *P. foliosus* auct.;
    P. semifructus auct.
15 P. berchtoldii Fieb.
    P. lacustris (Pearsall & Pearsall f.) Druce; *P. millardii* H.-Harrison; *P. pusillus* auct.; *P. franconicus* auct.; *P. trinervius* auct.
    P. berchtoldii × coloratus=P. × lanceolatus Sm.
    P. perpygmaeus Hagstr. ex Druce
16 P. trichoides Cham. & Schlecht.
17 P. compressus L.
    P. zosteraefolius Schumach.
18 P. acutifolius Link
    P. acutifolius × friesii = P. × pseudofriesii Dandy & Taylor
    P. acutifolius × berchtoldii=P. × sudermanicus Hagstr.
19 P. crispus L.
    P. crispus × lucens=P. × cadburyae Dandy & Taylor
    P. crispus × praelongus=P. × undulatus Wolfg.
    P. crispus × perfoliatus=P. × cooperi (Fryer) Fryer
    P. crispus × friesii=P. × lintonii Fryer
    P. crispus × trichoides=P. × bennettii Fryer
20 P. filiformis Pers.
    P. marinus auct.
    P. filiformis × pectinatus=P. × suecicus K. Richt.
21 P. pectinatus L.
    P. interruptus Kit.; *P. flabellatus* Bab.; *P. suecicus* auct.

578 GROENLANDIA Gay

1 G. densa (L.) Fourr.
    Potamogeton densus L.

RUPPIACEAE

579 RUPPIA L.

1 R. spiralis L. ex Dumort.
    R. maritima auct.
2 R. maritima L.
    R. rostellata Koch

ZANNICHELLIACEAE
580 ZANNICHELLIA L.
   1 Z. palustris L.
      Z. polycarpa Nolte ex Reichb.; *Z. gibberosa* Reichb.;
      Z. pedunculata Reichb.; *Z. pedicellata* Fr.;
      Z. maritima Nolte ex G. F. W. Mey.; *Z. brachy-stemon* Gay ex Reut.

NAJADACEAE
581 NAJAS L.
   1 N. flexilis (Willd.) Rostk. & Schmidt
   2†*N. graminea Del.
   3 N. marina L.

ERIOCAULACEAE
582 ERIOCAULON L.
   1 E. septangulare With.

LILIACEAE
583 TOFIELDIA Huds.
   1 T. pusilla (Michx.) Pers.
      T. palustris Huds. *pro parte*; *T. borealis* (Wahlenb.)
      Wahlenb.

584 NARTHECIUM Huds.
   1 N. ossifragum (L.) Huds.

585 SIMETHIS Kunth
   Pubilaria Raf.
   1 S. planifolia (L.) Gren. & Godr.
      S. bicolor (Desf.) Kunth; *Pubilaria planifolia* (L.)
      Druce

586 *HEMEROCALLIS L.
   1 *H. fulva (L.) L.
   2 *H. lilioasphodelus L.
      H. flava (L.) L.

587 *PHORMIUM J. R. & G. Forst.
   1 *P. tenax J. R. & G. Forst.

588 CONVALLARIA L.
   1 C. majalis L.

589 POLYGONATUM Mill.
    1   P. verticillatum (L.) All.
    2   P. odoratum (Mill.) Druce
          P. officinale All.; *P. anceps* Moench; *P. polygonatum*
          (L.) Voss
    3   P. multiflorum (L.) All.
      *P. multiflorum × odoratum = P. × hybridum Brügger

590 MAIANTHEMUM Weber
      Unifolium Ludw.
    1   M. bifolium (L.) Schmidt
          M. convallaria Weber; *Unifolium bifolium* (L.)
          Greene

591 ASPARAGUS L.
    1   A. officinalis L.
      a   *subsp. officinalis
      b   subsp. prostratus (Dumort.) E. F. Warb.
          A. maritimus Mill. *pro parte*

592 RUSCUS L.
    1   R. aculeatus L.

593 *LILIUM L.
    1   *L. martagon L.
    2   *L. pyrenaicum Gouan

594 FRITILLARIA L.
    1   F. meleagris L.

595 *TULIPA L.
    1   *T. sylvestris L.

596 LLOYDIA Salisb. ex Reichb.
    1   L. serotina (L.) Reichb.

597 GAGEA Salisb.
    1   G. lutea (L.) Ker-Gawl.

598 ORNITHOGALUM L.
    1   O. umbellatum L.
    2   *O. nutans L.
    3   O. pyrenaicum L.

599 SCILLA L.
    1 S. verna Huds.
    2 S. autumnalis L.

600 ENDYMION Dumort.
    1 E. non-scriptus (L.) Garcke
        Scilla nutans Sm.; *S. non-scripta* (L.) Hoffmanns. &
        Link
    2 *E. hispanicus (Mill.) Chouard
        Scilla hispanica Mill.

601 MUSCARI Mill.
    1 M. atlanticum Boiss. & Reut.
        M. racemosum auct.
    2 *M. comosum (L.) Mill.
        Hyacinthus comosus L.

602 COLCHICUM L.
    1 C. autumnale L.

603 PARIS L.
    1 P. quadrifolia L.

*PONTEDERIACEAE

604 *PONTEDERIA L.
    1 *P. cordata L.

JUNCACEAE

605 JUNCUS L.
    1 J. squarrosus L.
    2 *J. tenuis Willd.
        J. macer Gray
    3 *J. dudleyi Wiegand
    4 J. compressus Jacq.
        J. compressus × gerardii
    5 J. gerardii Lois.
    6 J. trifidus L.
    7 J. bufonius L.
    8 J. inflexus L.
        J. glaucus Sibth.
    9 J. effusus L.
        J. communis auct.
        J. effusus × inflexus = J. × diffusus Hoppe

138

10 J. conglomeratus L.
     J. communis E. Mey.; *J. leersii* Marsson
     J. conglomeratus × effusus
11 *J. pallidus R. Br.
12 J. filiformis L.
13 J. balticus Willd.
14 J. maritimus Lam.
     J. spinosus auct.
15 J. acutus L.
16 J. capitatus Weigel
17 J. subnodulosus Schrank
     J. obtusiflorus Ehrh. ex Hoffm.
18 J. acutiflorus Ehrh. ex Hoffm.
     J. sylvaticus auct.
     J. acutiflorus × articulatus=J. × surrejanus Druce
19 J. articulatus L.
     J. lampocarpus Ehrh. ex Hoffm.; *J. nigritellus* D. Don
20 J. alpinoarticulatus Chaix
     J. alpinus Vill.; *J. nodulosus* auct.
     J. alpinoarticulatus × articulatus
21 J. nodulosus Wahlenb.
     J. marshallii Pugsl.
22 J. bulbosus L.
     J. supinus Moench; *J. kochii* F. W. Schultz
23 J. mutabilis Lam.
     J. pygmaeus Rich.
24 J. castaneus Sm.
25 J. biglumis L.
26 J. triglumis L.

606 LUZULA DC.
     Juncoides Adans.
1 L. pilosa (L.) Willd.
     L. vernalis (Reichard) DC.; *Juncoides pilosa* (L.) Kuntze
2 L. forsteri (Sm.) DC.
     Juncoides forsteri (Sm.) Kuntze
     L. forsteri × pilosa=L. × borreri Bromf. ex Bab.
     Juncoides pilosa var. *borreri* (Bab.) Druce
3 L. sylvatica (Huds.) Gaudin
     L. maxima (Reichard) DC.; *Juncoides sylvatica* (Huds.) Kuntze

139

4 *L. luzuloides (Lam.) Dandy & Wilmott
    L. albida (Hoffm.) DC.; *L. nemorosa* (Poll.) E. Mey.,
      non Hornem.; *Juncoides nemorosa* (Poll.) Kuntze
5 *L. nivea (L.) DC.
    Juncoides nivea (L.) Kuntze
6 L. spicata (L.) DC.
    Juncoides spicata (L.) Kuntze
7 L. arcuata Sw.
    Juncoides arcuata (Sw.) Kuntze
8 L. campestris (L.) DC.
    Juncoides campestris (L.) Kuntze
9 L. multiflora (Retz.) Lejeune
    L. erecta Desv.; *Juncoides multiflora* (Retz.) Druce
10 L. pallescens Sw.
    Juncoides pallescens (Sw.) Druce

AMARYLLIDACEAE

607 ALLIUM L.

  1 A. ampeloprasum L.
  2 A. babingtonii Borrer
  3 A. scorodoprasum L.
  4 A. sphaerocephalon L.
  5 A. vineale L.
  6 A. oleraceum L.
  7 *A. carinatum L.
  8 A. schoenoprasum L.
     A. sibiricum L.
  9 *A. roseum L.
    a *subsp. roseum
    b *subsp. bulbiferum (DC.) E. F. Warb.
     A. ambiguum Sm., non DC.
10 *A. triquetrum L.
11 *A. paradoxum (Bieb.) G. Don
12 A. ursinum L.

608 *NOTHOSCORDUM Kunth

  1 *N. inodorum (Ait.) Nicholson

609 *IPHEION Raf.

  1 *I. uniflorum (Grah.) Raf.
    Milla uniflora Grah.

610 *AGAPANTHUS L'Hérit.
    1 *A. orientalis F. M. Leighton

611 LEUCOJUM L.
    1 L. vernum L.
    2 L. aestivum L.
        L. pulchellum Salisb.

612 GALANTHUS L.
    1 G. nivalis L.

613 [*STERNBERGIA Waldst. & Kit.]
    1 [*S. lutea (L.) Ker-Gawl. ex Spreng.]

614 NARCISSUS L.
    1 N. pseudonarcissus L.
    2 *N. obvallaris Salisb.
        N. lobularis (Haw.) J. A. & J. H. Schult.
    3 *N. hispanicus Gouan
        N. major Curt.
    4 *N. × incomparabilis Mill.
    5 *N. × infundibulum Poir.
        N. odorus auct.
    6 *N. majalis Curt.
        N. poeticus auct.
    7 *N. × biflorus Curt.

IRIDACEAE

615 SISYRINCHIUM L.
    1 S. bermudiana L.
        S. angustifolium Mill.
    2 *S. californicum (Ker-Gawl.) Ait. f.

616 IRIS L.
    1 *I. spuria L.
    2 *I. versicolor L.
    3 I. foetidissima L.
    4 I. pseudacorus L.
    5 *I. germanica L.

617 *HERMODACTYLUS Mill.
    1 *H. tuberosus (L.) Mill.
        Iris tuberosa L.

618 *CROCUS L.
> 1 *C. nudiflorus Sm.
> 2 *C. purpureus Weston
>> *C. officinalis* Huds. *pro parte*; *C. vernus* auct.; *C. albiflorus* auct.
> 3 *C. sativus L.
> 4 *C. biflorus Mill.
> 5 *C. flavus Weston
>> *C. aureus* Sm.

619 ROMULEA Maratti
> 1 R. columnae Seb. & Mauri
>> *R. parviflora* Bub.

620 *CROCOSMIA Planch.
> 1 *C. × crocosmiflora (Lemoine) N. E. Br.
>> *Tritonia crocosmiflora* (Lemoine) Nicholson

621 GLADIOLUS L.
> 1 G. illyricus Koch
>> *G. communis* auct.
> 2 *G. byzantinus Mill.
> 3 *G. segetum Ker-Gawl.

DIOSCOREACEAE
622 TAMUS L.
> 1 T. communis L.

CYPRIPEDIACEAE
623 CYPRIPEDIUM L.
> 1 C. calceolus L.

ORCHIDACEAE
624 CEPHALANTHERA Rich.
> 1 C. damasonium (Mill.) Druce
>> *C. pallens* Rich.; *C. grandiflora* Gray; *C. latifolia* Janchen
> 2 C. longifolia (L.) Fritsch
>> *C. ensifolia* (Schmidt) Rich.
> 3 C. rubra (L.) Rich.

ORCHIDACEAE

625 EPIPACTIS Sw.
Helleborine Mill.

1 E. palustris (L.) Crantz
    E. longifolia All.; *Helleborine palustris* (L.) Schrank
2 E. helleborine (L.) Crantz
    E. latifolia (L.) All.; *Helleborine helleborine* (L.)
    Druce; *Epipactis media* auct.
    E. helleborine × purpurata = E. × schulzei P. Fourn.
    Helleborine schulzei (P. Fourn.) P. M. Hall
3 E. purpurata Sm.
    E. sessilifolia Peterm.; *E. violacea* (Dur. Duq.) Bor.;
    Helleborine purpurata (Sm.) Druce
4 E. leptochila (Godfery) Godfery
    E. viridiflora var. *leptochila* Godfery; *Helleborine*
    leptochila (Godfery) Druce; *Epipactis cleistogama*
    C. Thomas
5 E. dunensis (T. & T. A. Stephenson) Godfery
    E. viridiflora var. *dunensis* (T. & T. A. Stephenson)
    Wilmott
6 E. phyllanthes G. E. Sm.
    E. viridiflora var. *vectensis* (T. & T. A. Stephenson)
    Wilmott; *E. vectensis* (T. & T. A. Stephenson)
    Brooke & Rose; *E. pendula* C. Thomas, non
    A. A. Eaton; *E. cambrensis* C. Thomas
7 E. atrorubens (Hoffm.) Schult.
    E. atropurpurea Raf.; *Helleborine atropurpurea*
    (Raf.) Schinz & Thell.
    E. atrorubens × helleborine = E. × schmalhausenii K.
    Richt.
    Helleborine schmalhausenii (K. Richt.) Vollmann

626 EPIPOGIUM R. Br.

1 E. aphyllum Sw.
    E. gmelini Rich.; *E. epipogium* (L.) Karst.

627 SPIRANTHES Rich.

1 S. spiralis (L.) Chevall.
    S. autumnalis Rich.
2 S. aestivalis (Poir.) Rich.
3 S. romanzoffiana Cham.
    S. gemmipara (Sm.) Lindl.; *S. stricta* (Rydb.) A. Nels.

143

ORCHIDACEAE

628 LISTERA R. Br.
  1 L. ovata (L.) R. Br.
  2 L. cordata (L.) R. Br.

629 NEOTTIA Ludw.
  1 N. nidus-avis (L.) Rich.

630 GOODYERA R. Br.
  1 G. repens (L.) R. Br.

631 HAMMARBYA Kuntze
  1 H. paludosa (L.) Kuntze
     Malaxis paludosa (L.) Sw.

632 LIPARIS Rich.
  1 L. loeselii (L.) Rich.

633 CORALLORHIZA Chatel.
  1 C. trifida Chatel.
     C. neotia Scop.; *C. innata* R. Br.

634 HERMINIUM R. Br.
  1 H. monorchis (L.) R. Br.

635 COELOGLOSSUM Hartm.
  1 C. viride (L.) Hartm.
     Habenaria viridis (L.) R. Br.

COELOGLOSSUM × GYMNADENIA = × GYMNAGLOS-SUM Rolfe
  C. viride × G. conopsea = × Gymnaglossum jacksonii
  (Quirk) Rolfe
  Habenaria jacksonii (Quirk) Druce

COELOGLOSSUM × DACTYLORCHIS
  C. viride × D. fuchsii
  Orchicoeloglossum mixtum Aschers. & Graebn.;
    Habenaria mixta (Aschers. & Graebn.) Druce
  C. viride × D. maculata
  Habenaria websteri Druce

C. viride × D. incarnata
C. viride × D. praetermissa
Orchicoeloglossum dominianum auct.
C. viride × D. purpurella
Orchis viridella H.-Harrison f.

636 GYMNADENIA R. Br.

1 G. conopsea (L.) R. Br.
Habenaria conopsea (L.) Benth., non Reichb. f.; *H. gymnadenia* Druce
a subsp. conopsea
b subsp. densiflora (Wahlenb.) G. Camus, Bergon & A. Camus
2 ‡G. odoratissima (L.) Rich.
Habenaria odoratissima (L.) Benth.

GYMNADENIA × LEUCORCHIS = × GYMLEUCORCHIS T. & T. A. Stephenson

G. conopsea × L. albida = × Gymleucorchis schweinfurthii (A. Kerner) T. & T. A. Stephenson
Habenaria schweinfurthii (A. Kerner) Druce, non Reichb. f.

637 LEUCORCHIS E. Mey.

1 L. albida (L.) E. Mey. ex Schur
Habenaria albida (L.) R. Br.; *Gymnadenia albida* (L.) Rich.

638 PLATANTHERA Rich.

1 P. chlorantha (Custer) Reichb.
Habenaria chlorantha (Custer) Bab., non Spreng.; *H. chloroleuca* Ridl.; *H. virescens* Druce, non Spreng.; *H. montana* auct.
2 P. bifolia (L.) Rich.
Habenaria bifolia (L.) R. Br.
P. bifolia × chlorantha = P. × hybrida Brügger
Habenaria hybrida Druce

639 NEOTINEA Reichb. f.

1 N. intacta (Link) Reichb. f.
Habenaria intacta (Link) Lindl. ex Benth.

640   OPHRYS L.

1   O. apifera Huds.
      O. trollii Hegetschw.
      O. apifera × fuciflora = O. × albertiana Camus
      O. botteroni auct.
      O. apifera × sphegodes = O. × pseudoapifera Caldesio
      O. epeirophora Peter
2   O. fuciflora (Crantz) Moench
      O. arachnites (L.) Reichard
      O. fuciflora × sphegodes = O. × obscura G. Beck
      O. aschersoni Nanteuil
3   O. sphegodes Mill.
      O. aranifera Huds.
4   O. insectifera L.
      O. muscifera Huds.
      O. insectifera × sphegodes = O. × hybrida Pokorny

641   HIMANTOGLOSSUM Spreng.

1   H. hircinum (L.) Spreng.
      Orchis hircina (L.) Crantz

642   ORCHIS L.

1   O. purpurea Huds.
2   O. militaris L.
      O. militaris × simia = O. × beyrichii A. Kerner
3   O. simia Lam.
4   O. ustulata L.
5   O. morio L.
6   [O. laxiflora Lam.]
      [O. laxiflora × morio = O. × alata Fleury]
7   O. mascula (L.) L.
      O. mascula × morio = O. × morioides Brand
      O. vilmsii Camus, non K. Richt.

643   DACTYLORCHIS (Klinge) Vermeul.

1   D. fuchsii (Druce) Vermeul.
      Orchis fuchsii Druce
   a   subsp. fuchsii
            Orchis maculata auct.
   b   subsp. okellyi (Druce) Vermeul.
            Orchis okellyi (Druce) Druce

146

c   subsp. hebridensis (Wilmott) H.-Harrison f.
       Orchis hebridensis Wilmott; *O. fuchsii* subsp.
       hebridensis (Wilmott) Clapham

D. fuchsii × maculata
   Orchis transiens Druce

D. fuchsii × incarnata
   Orchis curtisiana Druce

D. fuchsii × praetermissa
   Orchis mortonii Druce

D. fuchsii × purpurella
   Orchis venusta T. & T. A. Stephenson; *O. hebridella*
   Wilmott

2 D. maculata (L.) Vermeul.

    a   subsp. rhoumensis (H.-Harrison f.) H.-Harrison f.
        Orchis fuchsii subsp. *rhoumensis* H.-Harrison f.

    b   subsp. ericetorum (E. F. Linton) Vermeul.
        Orchis ericetorum (E. F. Linton) E. S. Marshall;
        O. maculata auct.; *O. elodes* auct.

D. maculata × praetermissa
   Orchis hallii Druce

D. maculata × purpurella
   Orchis formosa T. & T. A. Stephenson

D. maculata × majalis
   Orchis dinglensis Wilmott

3 D. incarnata (L.) Vermeul.
    Orchis incarnata L.; *O. latifolia* auct.

    a   subsp. incarnata
        Orchis strictifolia Opiz

    b   subsp. pulchella (Druce) H.-Harrison f.

    c   subsp. coccinea (Pugsl.) H.-Harrison f.
        Orchis strictifolia subsp. *coccinea* (Pugsl.)
        Clapham

    d   subsp. cruenta (O. F. Muell.) Vermeul.
        Orchis cruenta O. F. Muell.

    e   subsp. gemmana (Pugsl.) H.-Harrison f.

    f   subsp. ochroleuca (Boll) H.-Harrison f.

D. incarnata × maculata

D. incarnata × praetermissa

D. incarnata × purpurella
   Orchis latirella P. M. Hall

4 D. praetermissa (Druce) Vermeul.
    Orchis praetermissa Druce; *O. pardalina* Pugsl.;
    O. latifolia auct.

5   D. purpurella (T. & T. A. Stephenson) Vermeul.
      Orchis purpurella T. & T. A. Stephenson
6   D. majalis (Reichb.) Vermeul.
        subsp. occidentalis (Pugsl.) H.-Harrison f.
          Orchis majalis subsp. *occidentalis* (Pugsl.)
          Pugsl.; *O. kerryensis* Wilmott; *O. occidentalis*
          (Pugsl.) Wilmott; *Dactylorchis kerryensis*
          (Wilmott) Vermeul.; *D. occidentalis* (Pugsl.)
          Vermeul.; *Orchis occidentalis* subsp. *kerry-*
          ensis (Wilmott) Clapham
7   D. traunsteineri (Sauter) Vermeul.
          Orchis traunsteineri Sauter; *O. majalis* subsp.
          traunsteinerioides Pugsl.; *O. traunsteinerioides*
          (Pugsl.) Pugsl.; *Dactylorchis traunsteinerioides*
          (Pugsl.) Vermeul.

DACTYLORCHIS × GYMNADENIA

D. fuchsii × G. conopsea
  Orchigymnadenia heinzeliana (Reichardt) Camus
D. maculata × G. conopsea
  Orchigymnadenia evansii (Druce) T. & T. A.
  Stephenson; *Habenaria evansii* (Druce) Druce
D. incarnata × G. conopsea
D. praetermissa × G. conopsea
  Habenaria wintoni Druce; *Orchigymnadenia wintoni*
  (Druce) Tahourdin; *Habenaria quirkiana* Druce
D. purpurella × G. conopsea
  Orchigymnadenia varia T. & T. A. Stephenson;
  Habenaria varia (T. & T. A. Stephenson) Druce

DACTYLORCHIS × PLATANTHERA

D. fuchsii × P. bifolia
D. maculata × P. bifolia
  Orchiplatanthera chevallieriana (Camus) Camus;
  Habenaria chevallieriana (Camus) Druce

644 ACERAS R. Br.
  1   A. anthropophorum (L.) Ait. f.

645 ANACAMPTIS Rich.
  1   A. pyramidalis (L.) Rich.
        Orchis pyramidalis L.

ANACAMPTIS × GYMNADENIA = × GYMNANACAMPTIS
Aschers. & Graebn.

    A. pyramidalis × G. conopsea = × Gymnanacamptis
      anacamptis (Wilms) Aschers. & Graebn.
    Gymnanacamptis aschersonii G. Camus, Bergon &
      A. Camus; *Habenaria anacamptis* (Wilms) Druce

ARACEAE
646 *ACORUS L.
    1 *A. calamus L.

647 *CALLA L.
    1 *C. palustris L.

648 *LYSICHITON Schott
    1 *L. americanus Hultén & St. John

649 ARUM L.
    1 A. maculatum L.
    2 A. italicum Mill.
        A. neglectum (Townsend) Ridl.
        A. italicum × maculatum

LEMNACEAE
650 LEMNA L.
    1 L. polyrhiza L.
    2 L. trisulca L.
    3 L. minor L.
    4 L. gibba L.

651 WOLFFIA Hork. ex Schleid.
    1 W. arrhiza (L.) Hork. ex Wimm.
      Lemna arrhiza L.

SPARGANIACEAE
652 SPARGANIUM L.
    1 S. erectum L.
    a subsp. erectum
        S. ramosum Huds.
    b subsp. neglectum (Beeby) Schinz & Thell.
        S. neglectum Beeby; *S. ramosum* subsp. *neglectum*
        (Beeby) Neum.

2 S. emersum Rehm.
    S. simplex Huds. *pro parte*
    S. emersum × erectum = S. × aschersonianum Hausskn.
3 S. angustifolium Michx.
    S. affine Schnizl.; *S. natans* auct.
    S. angustifolium × emersum
4 S. minimum Wallr.

TYPHACEAE

653 TYPHA L.

1 T. latifolia L.
2 T. angustifolia L.
    T. angustifolia × latifolia = T. × glauca Godr.

CYPERACEAE

654 ERIOPHORUM L.

1 E. angustifolium Honck.
    E. polystachion L., *nom. ambig.*
2 E. gracile Roth
3 E. latifolium Hoppe
    E. paniculatum Druce; *E. polystachion* auct.
4 E. vaginatum L.
    E. opacum auct.; *E. brachyantherum* auct.

655 SCIRPUS L.

    Trichophorum Pers.; *Isolepis* R. Br.; *Eleogiton* Link;
    Holoschoenus Link; *Schoenoplectus* (Reichb.) Palla

1 †S. hudsonianus (Michx.) Fernald
    Eriophorum alpinum L.; *Trichophorum alpinum* (L.)
    Pers.
2 S. cespitosus L.
    Trichophorum cespitosum (L.) Hartm.
  a   subsp. cespitosus
  b   subsp. germanicus (Palla) Broddesson
        S. germanicus (Palla) Lindm.; *Trichophorum*
        cespitosum subsp. *germanicum* (Palla) Hegi
3 S. maritimus L.
4 S. sylvaticus L.
5 S. holoschoenus L.
    Holoschoenus vulgaris Link

150

6　S. triquetrus L.
　　Schoenoplectus triquetrus (L.) Pall
7　[S. americanus Pers.
　　S. pungens Vahl; *Schoenoplectus americanus* (Pers.)
　　Volkart]
8　S. lacustris L.
　　Schoenoplectus lacustris (L.) Palla
　　S. lacustris×triquetrus=S.×carinatus Sm.
　　Schoenoplectus carinatus (Sm.) Palla
9　S. tabernaemontani C. C. Gmel.
　　Schoenoplectus tabernaemontani (C. C. Gmel.)
　　Palla
　　S. tabernaemontani × triquetrus=S. × kuekenthali-
　　anus Junge
　　S. arunensis Druce
10　S. setaceus L.
　　Isolepis setacea (L.) R. Br.
11　S. cernuus Vahl
　　S. filiformis Savi, non Burm. f.; *Isolepis cernua* (Vahl)
　　Roem. & Schult.; *Scirpus savii* Seb. & Mauri; *S.
　　pygmaeus* (Vahl) A. Gray, non Lam.
12　S. fluitans L.
　　Eleogiton fluitans (L.) Link

656　ELEOCHARIS R. Br.
1　E. parvula (Roem. & Schult.) Link ex Bluff, Nees &
　　Schau.
　　Scirpus nanus Spreng., non Poir.; *S. parvulus* Roem.
　　& Schult.
2　E. acicularis (L.) Roem. & Schult.
　　Scirpus acicularis L.
3　E. quinqueflora (F. X. Hartmann) Schwarz
　　Scirpus pauciflorus Lightf.; *Eleocharis pauciflora*
　　(Lightf.) Link
4　E. multicaulis (Sm.) Sm.
　　Scirpus multicaulis Sm.
5　E. palustris (L.) Roem. & Schult.
　　Scirpus palustris L.
　a　subsp. palustris
　b　subsp. microcarpa Walters
6　E. uniglumis (Link) Schult.
　　Scirpus uniglumis Link; *Eleocharis watsoni* Bab.

CYPERACEAE

657 BLYSMUS Panz.

    1 B. compressus (L.) Panz. ex Link
        Scirpus caricis Retz.; *S. compressus* (L.) Pers., non
        Moench
    2 B. rufus (Huds.) Link
        Scirpus rufus (Huds.) Schrad.

658 CYPERUS L.

    1 C. longus L.
    2 C. fuscus L.

659 SCHOENUS L.

    1 S. nigricans L.
    2 S. ferrugineus L.

660 RHYNCHOSPORA Vahl

    1 R. alba (L.) Vahl
    2 R. fusca (L.) Ait. f.

661 CLADIUM Browne
    Mariscus Zinn, non Gaertn.

    1 C. mariscus (L.) Pohl
        Mariscus mariscus (L.) Borbás

662 KOBRESIA Willd.

    1 K. simpliciuscula (Wahlenb.) Mackenzie
        K. caricina Willd.; *K. bipartita* auct.

663 CAREX L.

    1 C. laevigata Sm.
        C. helodes Link
    2 C. distans L.
        C. distans × hostiana=C. × muellerana F. W. Schultz
        C. distans × extensa=C. × tornabenii Chiov.
    3 C. punctata Gaudin
    4 C. hostiana DC.
        C. hornschuchiana Hoppe; *C. fulva* auct.
        C. hostiana × lepidocarpa=C. × fulva Gooden.
        C. leutzii Kneuck.
        C. hostiana × serotina
    5 C. binervis Sm.
        C. sadleri E. F. Linton; *C. frigida* auct.

     C. binervis × punctata
     C. binervis × hostiana
     C. binervis × demissa＝C. × corstorphinei Druce

6   C. flava L.
7   C. lepidocarpa Tausch
   a   subsp. lepidocarpa
   b   subsp. scotica E. W. Davies
     C. lepidocarpa × serotina＝C. × schatzii Kneuck.
8   C. demissa Hornem.
       C. tumidicarpa Anderss.
     C. demissa × hostiana
     C. demissa × lepidocarpa
     C. demissa × serotina
9   C. scandinavica E. W. Davies
10 C. serotina Mérat
       C. oederi auct.
11 C. extensa Gooden.
12 C. sylvatica Huds.
13 C. capillaris L.
14 C. depauperata Curt. ex With.
15 C. pseudocyperus L.
     C. pseudocyperus × rostrata
16 C. rostrata Stokes
       C. ampullacea Gooden.; *C. inflata* auct.
     C. rostrata × vesicaria＝C. × involuta (Bab.) Syme
       C. pannewitziana Figert
17 C. vesicaria L.
18 C. stenolepis Less.
       C. grahami Boott
19 C. saxatilis L.
       C. pulla Gooden.
     C. saxatilis × stenolepis＝C. × ewingii E. S. Marshall
20 C. riparia Curt.
     C. riparia × vesicaria＝C. × csomadensis Simonk.
21 C. acutiformis Ehrh.
       C. paludosa Gooden.
     C. acutiformis × rostrata＝C. × beckmanniana Figert
22 C. pendula Huds.
23 C. strigosa Huds.
24 C. pallescens L.
25 C. filiformis L.
       C. tomentosa auct.
26 C. panicea L.

27　C. vaginata Tausch
28　C. limosa L.
29　C. paupercula Michx.
　　　C. irrigua (Wahlenb.) Sm. ex Hoppe; *C. magellanica*
　　　auct.
30　C. rariflora (Wahlenb.) Sm.
31　C. flacca Schreb.
　　　C. glauca Scop.; *C. diversicolor* auct.
32　C. hirta L.
　　　C. hirta × vesicaria = C. × grossii Fiek
33　C. lasiocarpa Ehrh.
　　　C. filiformis auct.
　　　C. lasiocarpa × riparia = C. × evoluta Hartm.
34　C. pilulifera L.
35　C. ericetorum Poll.
36　C. caryophyllea Latourr.
　　　C. praecox auct.
37　C. montana L.
38　C. humilis Leyss.
39　C. digitata L.
40　C. ornithopoda Willd.
41　‡C. glacialis Mackenzie
42　C. buxbaumii Wahlenb.
　　　C. canescens L., *nom. ambig.*; *C. polygama* Schkuhr,
　　　non J. F. Gmel.; *C. fusca* auct.
43　C. atrata L.
44　C. norvegica Retz.
　　　C. alpina Liljeb., non Schrank; *C. halleri* auct.
45　C. atrofusca Schkuhr
　　　C. ustulata Wahlenb.
46　C. elata All.
　　　C. stricta Gooden., non Lam.; *C. hudsonii* A. Benn.
　　　C. elata × nigra = C. × turfosa Fr.
47　C. acuta L.
　　　C. gracilis Curt.
　　　C. acuta × acutiformis = C. × subgracilis Druce
　　　C. acuta × elata
　　　C. acuta × nigra = C. × elytroides Fr.
48　C. aquatilis Wahlenb.
　　　C. aquatilis × elata = C. × hibernica A. Benn.
　　　C. aquatilis × recta = C. × grantii A. Benn.
　　　C. aquatilis × nigra
　　　C. aquatilis × bigelowii = C. × limula Fr.

49 C. recta Boott
        C. kattegatensis Fr. ex Krecz.; *C. salina* auct.
50 C. nigra (L.) Reichard
        C. fusca All.; *C. goodenowii* Gay; *C. gibsoni* Bab.;
            C. eboracensis Nelmes; *C. juncella* auct.
     C. nigra × recta
51 C. trinervis Degl.
52 C. bigelowii Torr. ex Schwein.
        C. rigida Gooden., non Schrank; *C. concolor* auct.
     C. bigelowii × nigra = C. × decolorans Wimm.
53 ‡C. bicolor All.
54 C. paniculata L.
     C. paniculata × remota = C. × boenninghausiana Weihe
55 C. appropinquata Schumach.
        C. paradoxa Willd., non J. F. Gmel.
     C. appropinquata × paniculata = C. × solstitialis Figert
56 C. diandra Schrank
        C. teretiuscula Gooden.
57 C. otrubae Podp.
        C. vulpina auct.
     C. otrubae × paniculata
     C. otrubae × spicata = C. × haussknechtii Senay
     C. otrubae × remota = C. × pseudoaxillaris K. Richt.
        C. axillaris Gooden., non L.; *C. kneuckeriana* Zahn
58 C. vulpina L.
59 *C. vulpinoidea Michx.
60 C. disticha Huds.
61 C. arenaria L.
62 C. divisa Huds.
63 C. chordorrhiza L. f.
64 C. maritima Gunn.
        C. incurva Lightf.
65 C. divulsa Stokes
     C. divulsa × otrubae
66 C. polyphylla Kar. & Kir.
        C. leersii F. W. Schultz, non Willd.
67 C. spicata Huds.
        C. contigua Hoppe; *C. muricata* auct.
68 C. muricata L.
        C. pairaei F. W. Schultz
69 C. elongata L.
70 C. echinata Murr.
        C. stellulata Gooden.

155

71 C. remota L.
    C. remota × spicata
        C. pseudoaxillaris auct.
72 C. curta Gooden.
        C. canescens auct.; *C. vitilis* auct.
    C. curta × echinata=C. × biharica Simonk.
        C. tetrastachya Traunst. ex Sauter, non Scheele
    C. curta × lachenalii=C. × helvola Blytt ex Fr.
73 C. lachenalii Schkuhr
        C. leporina L., *nom. ambig.*; *C. lagopina* Wahlenb.
74 C. ovalis Gooden.
        C. leporina auct.
75 *C. crawfordii Fernald
76 C. rupestris All.
77 C. microglochin Wahlenb.
78 C. pauciflora Lightf.
79 ‡C. capitata L.
80 C. pulicaris L.
81 C. dioica L.
    C. dioica × echinata
82 †C. davalliana Sm.

GRAMINEAE

664 LEERSIA Sw.

1 L. oryzoides (L.) Sw.
        Oryza oryzoides (L.) Brand

665 PHRAGMITES Adans.

1 P. communis Trin.
        Arundo phragmites L.; *Phragmites phragmites* (L.)
        Karst.

666 *CORTADERIA Stapf

1 *C. selloana (J. A. & J. H. Schult.) Aschers. & Graebn.
        Gynerium argenteum Nees

667 MOLINIA Schrank

1 M. caerulea (L.) Moench

668 SIEGLINGIA Bernh.

1 S. decumbens (L.) Bernh.
        Triodia decumbens (L.) Beauv.

669 GLYCERIA R. Br.

1 G. fluitans (L.) R. Br.
Poa fluitans (L.) Scop.
G. fluitans × plicata = G. × pedicellata Townsend
2 G. plicata Fr.
3 G. declinata Bréb.
G. declinata × fluitans
4 G. maxima (Hartm.) Holmberg
Poa aquatica L.; *Glyceria aquatica* (L.) Wahlb., non
J. & C. Presl

670 FESTUCA L.

1 F. pratensis Huds.
F. elatior auct.
2 F. arundinacea Schreb.
F. elatior L., *nom. ambig.*
F. arundinacea × pratensis = F. × aschersoniana
Dörfl.
F. arundinacea × gigantea = F. × gigas Holmberg
3 F. gigantea (L.) Vill.
Bromus giganteus L.
F. gigantea × pratensis = F. × schlickumii Grantz.
4 F. altissima All.
F. silvatica Vill., non Huds.
5 *F. heterophylla Lam.
6 F. rubra L.
a subsp. rubra
F. arenaria Retz., non Lam.; *F. oraria* Dumort.
b subsp. commutata Gaudin
F. fallax Thuill.; *F. rubra* var. *fallax* (Thuill.)
Hack.
7 F. juncifolia St.-Amans
F. dumetorum auct.
8 F. ovina L.
F. sulcata auct.
9 F. tenuifolia Sibth.
F. ovina subsp. *tenuifolia* (Sibth.) Peterm.; *F. capillata*
auct.
10 F. vivipara (L.) Sm.
F. supina auct.

11   F. longifolia Thuill.
     F. trachyphylla (Hack.) Krajina, non Hack.; *F. duriuscula* auct.
12   F. glauca Lam.
     F. caesia Sm.

FESTUCA × LOLIUM = × FESTULOLIUM Aschers. & Graebn.
     F. pratensis × L. perenne = × Festulolium loliaceum (Huds.) P. Fourn.
     Festuca loliacea Huds.; *F. adscendens* Retz.
     F. pratensis × L. multiflorum = × Festulolium braunii (K. Richt.) A. Camus
     F. arundinacea × L. perenne = × Festulolium holmbergii (Dörfl.) P. Fourn.
     F. arundinacea × L. multiflorum
     F. gigantea × L. perenne = × Festulolium brinkmannii (A. Braun) Aschers. & Graebn.
     F. gigantea × L. multiflorum

FESTUCA × VULPIA
     F. rubra × V. membranacea
     F. rubra × V. myuros

671   LOLIUM L.

1   L. perenne L.
2   *L. multiflorum Lam.
     L. italicum A. Braun
     L. multiflorum × perenne = L. × hybridum Hausskn.
3   *L. temulentum L.

672   VULPIA C. C. Gmel.

1   V. membranacea (L.) Dumort.
     Festuca fasciculata Forsk.; *F. uniglumis* Ait.; *F. membranacea* (L.) Druce, non Kit.
2   V. bromoides (L.) Gray
     Festuca bromoides L.; *F. sciuroides* Roth
3   V. myuros (L.) C. C. Gmel.
     Festuca myuros L.
4   *V. megalura (Nutt.) Rydb.
5   V. ambigua (Le Gall) More
     Festuca ambigua Le Gall; *F. danthonii* var. *ambigua* (Le Gall) Druce

158

6 *V. ciliata Link
> *Festuca ciliata* Danthon ex DC., non Gouan; *F. danthonii* Aschers. & Graebn.

673 PUCCINELLIA Parl.

1 P. maritima (Huds.) Parl.
> *Poa maritima* Huds.; *Glyceria maritima* (Huds.) Wahlb.; *Sclerochloa maritima* (Huds.) Lindl. ex Bab.; *S. festuciformis* Britten & Rendle *pro parte*; *Glyceria burdoni* Druce; *G. festuciformis* auct.
>
> P. maritima × rupestris = P. × krusemaniana Jansen & Wachter

2 P. distans (L.) Parl.
> *Poa distans* L.; *Glyceria distans* (L.) Wahlenb.; *Sclerochloa distans* (L.) Bab.; *Glyceria pulvinata* Druce *pro parte*
>
> P. distans × maritima = P. × hybrida Holmberg
> *Glyceria salina* Druce
>
> P. distans × rupestris = P. × pannonica (Hack.) Holmberg

3 P. pseudodistans (Crép.) Jansen & Wachter
4 P. fasciculata (Torr.) Bicknell
> *Glyceria borreri* (Bab.) Bab.; *Sclerochloa borreri* (Bab.) Bab.

5 P. rupestris (With.) Fernald & Weatherby
> *Poa rupestris* With.; *Glyceria procumbens* (Curt.) Dumort.; *Sclerochloa rupestris* (With.) Britten & Rendle; *Glyceria rupestris* (With.) E. S. Marshall

674 CATAPODIUM Link
Scleropoa Griseb.

1 C. rigidum (L.) C. E. Hubbard
> *Poa rigida* L.; *Sclerochloa rigida* (L.) Link; *Festuca rigida* (L.) Rasp., non Roth; *Scleropoa rigida* (L.) Griseb.; *Demazeria rigida* (L.) Tutin

2 C. marinum (L.) C. E. Hubbard
> *Poa loliacea* Huds.; *Festuca rottboellioides* Kunth; *Sclerochloa loliacea* Woods ex Bab.; *Demazeria loliacea* Nyman; *D. marina* (L.) Druce; *Festuca loliacea* auct.

675 NARDURUS (Bluff, Nees & Schau.) Reichb.

1 N. maritimus (L.) Murb.
> *Festuca maritima* L.

159

676 POA L.

    1 P. annua L.
    2 P. infirma Kunth
        P. remotiflora (Hack.) Murb., non Rupr.; *P. exilis* (Tomm.) Murb.
    3 P. bulbosa L.
    4 P. alpina L.
        P. alpina × flexuosa=P. × jemtlandica (Almq.) K. Richt.
    5 P. flexuosa Sm.
        P. laxa auct.; *P. minor* auct.
    6 P. nemoralis L.
        P. parnellii Bab.
    7 P. glauca Vahl
        P. caesia Sm.
    8 P. balfourii Parnell
    9 P. compressa L.
    10 P. pratensis L.
    11 P. angustifolia L.
        P. strigosa Hoffm.; *P. pratensis* subsp. *angustifolia* (L.) Gaudin
    12 P. subcaerulea Sm.
        P. irrigata Lindm.; *P. pratensis* subsp. *irrigata* (Lindm.) Lindb. f.; *P. pratensis* subsp. *subcaerulea* (Sm.) Tutin; *P. pratensis* subsp. *alpigena* auct.
    13 P. trivialis L.
    14 *P. palustris L.
    15 *P. chaixii Vill.
        P. sylvatica Vill., non Poll.

677 CATABROSA Beauv.

    1 C. aquatica (L.) Beauv.

678 DACTYLIS L.

    1 D. glomerata L.
    2 *D. polygama Horvat.
        D. aschersoniana Graebn.

679 CYNOSURUS L.

    1 C. cristatus L.
    2 *C. echinatus L.

GRAMINEAE

680 BRIZA L.
  1 B. media L.
  2 *B. minor L.
  3 *B. maxima L.

681 MELICA L.
  1 M. uniflora Retz.
     M. nutans auct.
  2 M. nutans L.
     M. montana Huds.

682 SESLERIA Scop.
  1 S. caerulea (L.) Ard.
     subsp. calcarea (Čelak.) Hegi

683 BROMUS L.
     Ceratochloa Beauv.; *Serrafalcus* Parl.; *Anisantha* C. Koch
  1 B. erectus Huds.
     Zerna erecta (Huds.) Gray
  2 B. ramosus Huds.
     B. asper Murr.; *Zerna ramosa* (Huds.) Lindm.
  3 B. benekenii (Lange) Trimen
  4 *B. inermis Leyss.
     Zerna inermis (Leyss.) Lindm.
  5 B. sterilis L.
     Anisantha sterilis (L.) Nevski
  6 B. madritensis L.
     Anisantha madritensis (L.) Nevski
  7 *B. diandrus Roth
     B. gussonii Parl.; *Anisantha gussonii* (Parl.) Nevski;
       Bromus maximus auct.; *B. rigens* auct.
  8 *B. rigidus Roth
     Anisantha rigida (Roth) Hyland.
  9 *B. tectorum L.
     Anisantha tectorum (L.) Nevski
 10 B. mollis L.
     Serrafalcus mollis (L.) Parl.; *Bromus hordeaceus* auct.
 11 B. ferronii Mabille
     B. molliformis auct.
 12 B. thominii Hardouin
     ? *B. hordeaceus* L.
 13 B. lepidus Holmberg
     B. britannicus I. A. Williams

GRAMINEAE

14 B. racemosus L.
      Serrafalcus racemosus (L.) Parl.
15 B. commutatus Schrad.
      B. pratensis Ehrh. ex Hoffm., non Lam.; *Serrafalcus commutatus* (Schrad.) Bab.; *S. pratensis* Wilmott
16 B. interruptus (Hack.) Druce
17 *B. arvensis L.
      Serrafalcus arvensis (L.) Godr.
18 *B. secalinus L.
      Serrafalcus secalinus (L.) Bab.
19 *B. carinatus Hook. & Arn.
      Ceratochloa carinata (Hook. & Arn.) Tutin; *Bromus marginatus* auct.
20 *B. unioloides Kunth
      Ceratochloa unioloides (Willd.) Beauv.

684 BRACHYPODIUM Beauv.
  1 B. sylvaticum (Huds.) Beauv.
  2 B. pinnatum (L.) Beauv.

685 AGROPYRON Gaertn.
    Elytrigia Desv.; *Roegneria* C. Koch
  1 A. caninum (L.) Beauv.
      Triticum caninum L.; *Roegneria canina* (L.) Nevski
  2 A. donianum F. B. White
      Triticum donianum (F. B. White) Wilmott; *Roegneria doniana* (F. B. White) Melderis; *Triticum biflorum* auct.
  3 A. repens (L.) Beauv.
      Triticum repens L.; *Elytrigia repens* (L.) Nevski
  4 A. pungens (Pers.) Roem. & Schult.
      Triticum pungens Pers.; *Elytrigia pungens* (Pers.) Tutin
      A. pungens × repens = A. × oliveri Druce
      A. campestre auct.
  5 A. junceiforme (A. & D. Löve) A. & D. Löve
      Elytrigia junceiformis A. & D. Löve; *Triticum junceum* auct.; *Agropyron junceum* auct.
      A. junceiforme × repens = A. × laxum (Fr.) Tutin
      A. junceiforme × pungens = A. × obtusiusculum Lange
      A. hackelii Druce; *Triticum acutum* auct.; *Agropyron acutum* auct.

162

GRAMINEAE

AGROPYRON × HORDEUM= × AGROHORDEUM Camus ex
A. Camus

> A. repens × H. secalinum = × Agrohordeum langei
> (K. Richt.) Camus ex A. Camus

686 ELYMUS L.

    1   E. arenarius L.

687 HORDEUM L.

    1   H. secalinum Schreb.
        H. pratense Huds.; *H. nodosum* auct.
    2   H. murinum L.
    3   H. marinum Huds.
        H. maritimum Stokes
    4 *H. hystrix Roth
        H. gussonianum Parl.

688 HORDELYMUS (Jessen) Harz

    1   H. europaeus (L.) Harz
        Elymus europaeus L.; *Hordeum sylvaticum* Huds.;
        H. europaeum (L.) All.

689 KOELERIA Pers.

    1   K. cristata (L.) Pers.
        K. gracilis Pers.; *K. pseudocristata* Domin; *K. supra-
        arenaria* Domin; *K. britannica* Domin; *K. mixta*
        Domin; *K. glauca* auct.; *K. albescens* auct.
    2   K. vallesiana (Honck.) Bertol.

690 *GAUDINIA Beauv.

    1 *G. fragilis (L.) Beauv.

691 TRISETUM Pers.

    1   T. flavescens (L.) Beauv.
        Avena flavescens L.

692 *AVENA L.

    1 *A. fatua L.
        A. fatua × sativa (A. sativa L.)
    2 *A. ludoviciana Durieu
    3 *A. strigosa Schreb.

163

693 HELICTOTRICHON Bess.

    1 H. pratense (L.) Pilg.
        Avena pratensis L.; *A. alpina* Sm., non Honck.;
        Helictotrichon alpinum (Roem. & Schult.)
        Henrard
    2 H. pubescens (Huds.) Pilg.
        Avena pubescens Huds.

694 ARRHENATHERUM Beauv.

    1 A. elatius (L.) Beauv. ex J. & C. Presl
        A. avenaceum Beauv.; *A. bulbosum* (Willd.) C.
        Presl; *A. tuberosum* F. W. Schultz

695 HOLCUS L.

    1 H. lanatus L.
    2 H. mollis L.

696 DESCHAMPSIA Beauv.

    1 D. cespitosa (L.) Beauv.
        Aira cespitosa L.
    2 D. alpina (L.) Roem. & Schult.
        Aira alpina L.
    3 D. flexuosa (L.) Trin.
        Aira flexuosa L.
    4 D. setacea (Huds.) Hack.
        Aira setacea Huds.

697 AIRA L.

    1 A. praecox L.
    2 A. caryophyllea L.
    3 *A. multiculmis Dumort.

698 CORYNEPHORUS Beauv.
    Weingaertneria Bernh.

    1 C. canescens (L.) Beauv.
        Aira canescens L.; *Weingaertneria canescens* (L.)
        Bernh.

699 AMMOPHILA Host
    Psamma Beauv.

    1 A. arenaria (L.) Link
        A. arundinacea Host; *Psamma arenaria* (L.) Roem.
        & Schult.

GRAMINEAE

AMMOPHILA × CALAMAGROSTIS = × AMMOCALAMA-GROSTIS P. Fourn.

A. arenaria × C. epigejos = × Ammocalamagrostis baltica (Schrad.) P. Fourn.

Psamma baltica (Schrad.) Beauv. ex Roem. & Schult.; *Ammophila baltica* (Schrad.) Dumort.

700 CALAMAGROSTIS Adans.
Deyeuxia Clarion ex Beauv.

1 C. epigejos (L.) Roth
2 C. canescens (Weber) Roth
    C. lanceolata Roth; *C. calamagrostis* (L.) Karst.
    C. canescens × stricta
3 C. stricta (Timm) Koel.
    C. hookeri (Syme) Druce; *C. neglecta* auct.; *Deyeuxia neglecta* auct.
4 C. scotica (Druce) Druce
    C. strigosa auct.

701 AGROSTIS L.

1 A. setacea Curt.
2 A. canina L.
   a   subsp. canina
   b   subsp. montana (Hartm.) Hartm.
   A. canina × tenuis
   A. canina × stolonifera
3 A. tenuis Sibth.
    A. vulgaris With.; *A. capillaris* auct.
4 A. gigantea Roth
    A. nigra With.; *A. capillaris* var. *nigra* (With.) Druce
   A. gigantea × tenuis
   A. gigantea × stolonifera
5 A. stolonifera L.
    A. palustris Huds.; *A. densissima* (Hack.) Druce; *A. alba* auct.
   A. stolonifera × tenuis
6 *A. avenacea J. F. Gmel.
    Calamagrostis filiformis (Forst. f.) Pilg., non Griseb.
7 *A. scabra Willd.
    A. hyemalis auct.

GRAMINEAE

8 *A. semiverticillata (Forsk.) C. Chr.
  A. verticillata Vill.; *Polypogon semiverticillatus* (Forsk.) Hyland.
  A. semiverticillata × stolonifera

AGROSTIS × POLYPOGON = × AGROPOGON P. Fourn.

  A. stolonifera × P. monspeliensis = × Agropogon littoralis (Sm.) C. E. Hubbard
  Polypogon littoralis Sm.; *P. lutosus* auct.

702 **APERA** Adans.
  1 A. spica-venti (L.) Beauv.
     Agrostis spica-venti L.
  2 A. interrupta (L.) Beauv.
     Agrostis interrupta L.

703 **POLYPOGON** Desf.
  1 P. monspeliensis (L.) Desf.

704 **MIBORA** Adans.
     Chamagrostis Borkh. ex Wibel
  1 M. minima (L.) Desv.
     Chamagrostis minima (L.) Borkh. ex Wibel; *Mibora verna* Beauv.

705 **GASTRIDIUM** Beauv.
  1 G. ventricosum (Gouan) Schinz & Thell.
     G. lendigerum (L.) Desv.

706 *LAGURUS L.
  1 *L. ovatus L.

707 **PHLEUM** L.
  1 P. bertolonii DC.
     P. nodosum auct.
  2 P. pratense L.
  3 P. alpinum L.
     P. commutatum Gaudin
  4 P. phleoides (L.) Karst.
     P. phalaroides Koel.
  5 P. arenarium L.

166

GRAMINEAE

708 ALOPECURUS L.

   1 A. myosuroides Huds.
         A. agrestis L.
   2 A. pratensis L.
   3 A. geniculatus L.
         A. geniculatus × pratensis = A. × hybridus Wimm.
   4 A. aequalis Sobol.
         A. fulvus Sm.
         A. aequalis × geniculatus = A. × haussknechtianus
         Aschers. & Graebn.
   5 A. bulbosus Gouan
   6 A. alpinus Sm.

709 MILIUM L.

   1 M. effusum L.
   2 [M. scabrum Rich.]

710 *ORYZOPSIS Michx.
       Piptatherum Beauv.

   1 *O. miliacea (L.) Benth. & Hook. ex Aschers. &
         Schweinf.
         Piptatherum multiflorum (Cav.) Beauv.

711 HIEROCHLOE R. Br.
       Savastana Schrank, non Scop.

   1 H. odorata (L.) Beauv.
         H. borealis (Schrad.) Roem. & Schult.; *Savastana
         odorata* (L.) Scribn.

712 ANTHOXANTHUM L.

   1 A. odoratum L.
   2 *A. puelii Lecoq & Lamotte
         A. aristatum auct.

713 PHALARIS L.
       Digraphis Trin.

   1 P. arundinacea L.
         Digraphis arundinacea (L.) Trin.
   2 *P. canariensis L.
   3 [*P. minor Retz.]
   4 *P. paradoxa L.

GRAMINEAE

714 PARAPHOLIS C. E. Hubbard
    1 P. strigosa (Dumort.) C. E. Hubbard
         Lepturus filiformis auct.
    2 P. incurva (L.) C. E. Hubbard
         Lepturus incurvatus Trin.; *L. incurvus* (L.) Druce

715 NARDUS L.
    1 N. stricta L.

716 SPARTINA Schreb.
    1 S. maritima (Curt.) Fernald
         S. stricta (Ait.) Roth
    2 *S. alterniflora Lois.
         S. alterniflora×maritima=S.×townsendii H. & J.
         Groves

717 *CYNODON Rich.
      Capriola Adans.
    1 *C. dactylon (L.) Pers.
         Capriola dactylon (L.) Kuntze

718 *ECHINOCHLOA Beauv.
    1 *E. crus-galli (L.) Beauv.
         Panicum crus-galli L.

719 *DIGITARIA P. C. Fabr.
    1 *D. ischaemum (Schreb.) Muhl.
         Panicum ischaemum Schreb.; *Digitaria humifusa*
         Pers.; *Panicum glabrum* Gaudin; *P. humifusum*
         (Pers.) Kunth; *Digitaria linearis* Crép., non Pers.;
         Panicum lineare auct.
    2 *D. sanguinalis (L.) Scop.
         Panicum sanguinale L.

720 *SETARIA Beauv.
    1 *S. viridis (L.) Beauv.
         Panicum viride L.
    2 *S. verticillata (L.) Beauv.
         Panicum verticillatum L.
    3 *S. lutescens (Weigel) Hubbard
         S. glauca auct.; *Panicum glaucum* auct.

INDEX TO FAMILIES

169

INDEX TO GENERA

Italics indicate generic synonyms and generic names mentioned only in the synonymy of species. Bold-face numerals indicate the serial numbers of the genera.

170

INDEX TO GENERA

171

INDEX TO GENERA